INDIANS

BLACK HAWK, *Cleven*
OSCEOLA, *Clark*
POCAHONTAS, *Seymour*
PONTIAC, *Peckham*
SACAGAWEA, *Seymour*
SEQUOYAH, *Snow*
SITTING BULL, *Stevenson*
SQUANTO, *Stevenson*
TECUMSEH, *Stevenson*

NAVAL HEROES

DAVID FARRAGUT, *Long*
GEORGE DEWEY, *Long*
JOHN PAUL JONES, *Snow*
MATTHEW CALBRAITH PERRY, *Scharbach*
OLIVER HAZARD PERRY, *Long*
RAPHAEL SEMMES, *Snow*
STEPHEN DECATUR, *Smith*

NOTED WIVES and MOTHERS

ABIGAIL ADAMS, *Wagoner*
DOLLY MADISON, *Monsell*
ELEANOR ROOSEVELT, *Weil*
JESSIE FREMONT, *Wagoner*
MARTHA WASHINGTON, *Wagoner*
MARY TODD LINCOLN, *Wilkie*
NANCY HANKS, *Stevenson*
RACHEL JACKSON, *Govan*

SCIENTISTS and INVENTORS

ABNER DOUBLEDAY, *Dunham*
ALBERT EINSTEIN, *Hammontree*
ALECK BELL, *Widdemer*
CYRUS MCCORMICK, *Dobler*
ELI WHITNEY, *Snow*
ELIAS HOWE, *Corcoran*
ELIZABETH BLACKWELL, *Henry*
GAIL BORDEN, *Paradis*
GEORGE CARVER, *Stevenson*
GEORGE EASTMAN, *Henry*
GEORGE PULLMAN, *Myers*
GEORGE WESTINGHOUSE, *Dunham*
HENRY FORD, *Aird and Ruddiman*
JOHN AUDUBON, *Mason*
JOHN BURROUGHS, *Frisbee*
JOHN DEERE, *Bare*
JOHN FITCH, *Stevenson*
LEE DEFOREST, *Dobler*
LUTHER BURBANK, *Burt*
MARIA MITCHELL, *Melin*
ROBERT FULTON, *Henry*
ROBERT GODDARD, *Moore*

SAMU...
TOM...
WALTER REED, *Higgins*
WILBUR AND ORVILLE WRIGHT, *Stevenson*
WILL AND CHARLIE MAYO, *Hammontree*

SOCIAL and CIVIC LEADERS

BETSY ROSS, *Weil*
BOOKER T. WASHINGTON, *Stevenson*
CLARA BARTON, *Stevenson*
DAN BEARD, *Mason*
DOROTHEA DIX, *Melin*
FRANCES WILLARD, *Mason*
J. STERLING MORTON, *Moore*
JANE ADDAMS, *Wagoner*
JOHN PETER ZENGER, Long
JULIA WARD HOWE, *Wagoner*
JULIETTE LOW, *Higgins*
LILIUOKALANI, *Newman*
LUCRETIA MOTT, *Burnett*
MOLLY PITCHER, *Stevenson*
OLIVER WENDELL HOLMES, JR., *Dunham*
SUSAN ANTHONY, *Monsell*

SOLDIERS

ANTHONY WAYNE, *Stevenson*
BEDFORD FORREST, *Parks*
DAN MORGAN, *Bryant*
DOUGLAS MACARTHUR, *Long*
ETHAN ALLEN, *Winders*
FRANCIS MARION, *Steele*
GEORGE CUSTER, *Stevenson*
ISRAEL PUTNAM, *Stevenson*
JEB STUART, *Winders*
NATHANAEL GREENE, *Peckham*
ROBERT E. LEE, *Monsell*
SAM HOUSTON, *Stevenson*
TOM JACKSON, *Monsell*
U. S. GRANT, *Stevenson*
WILLIAM HENRY HARRISON, *Peckham*
ZACK TAYLOR, *Wilkie*

STATESMEN

ABE LINCOLN, *Stevenson*
ANDY JACKSON, *Stevenson*
DAN WEBSTER, *Smith*
FRANKLIN ROOSEVELT, *Weil*
HENRY CLAY, *Monsell*
HERBERT HOOVER, *Comfort*
JAMES MONROE, *Widdemer*
JEFF DAVIS, *de Grummond and Delaune*
JOHN F. KENNEDY, *Frisbee*
JOHN MARSHALL, *Monsell*
TEDDY ROOSEVELT, *Parks*
WOODROW WILSON, *Monsell*

Robert Frost

Boy with Promises to Keep

Illustrated by Al Fiorentino

Robert Frost

Boy with Promises to Keep

By Ellen Wilson

THE **BOBBS-MERRILL** COMPANY, INC.
A SUBSIDIARY OF HOWARD W. SAMS & CO., INC.
Publishers · INDIANAPOLIS · NEW YORK

for the
Cameron, Johnson, and Wilson
grandchildren

Grateful credit is given to Holt, Rinehart and Winston, Inc.; the Estate of Robert Frost; and Lawrance Thompson for permission to quote copyrighted material:

Portion of a letter from Robert Frost to Sabra Peabody dated September 1886 from SELECTED LETTERS OF ROBERT FROST edited by Lawrance Thompson. Copyright 1964 by Holt, Rinehart and Winston, Inc. Random lines from "La Noche Triste" by Robert Frost, and random lines in "The Tuft of Flowers," "Stopping by Woods on a Snowy Evening," and "The Gift Outright," from the COMPLETE POEMS OF ROBERT FROST. Copyrighted 1942, 1951, 1962 by Robert Frost.

Illustrations

Numerous smaller illustrations

Contents

Books by Ellen Wilson

ANNIE OAKLEY: LITTLE SURE SHOT
ERNIE PYLE: BOY FROM BACK HOME
ROBERT FROST: BOY WITH PROMISES TO KEEP

★ Robert Frost

Boy with Promises to Keep

Learning to Whistle

"Is THIS REALLY whistling?" Rob asked his father. He jumped down from the porch railing. Puckering his lips, he tried for the hundredth time to whistle. All he could do was make a whooshing sound.

"No, that's not real whistling, but it's almost," Mr. Frost said. "Simply keep trying. Any time now you'll get the knack of it, like this." Rob's father gave a long shrill whistle. It was loud enough to be heard all the way down on the waterfront of San Francisco.

Rob's little sister, Jeanie, came out on the porch. "What's the matter?" she asked.

11

Mama hurried out, too. "What's wrong, Will? What's wrong?" She looked at Rob's father, then at Rob. Her blue eyes were anxious.

Papa laughed. "Nothing's wrong. I'm just showing Rob how to whistle, that's all. Like this." Again Papa whistled almost as loud as a steam locomotive.

Mama and Jeanie clapped their hands over their ears. But Rob just smiled. He looked at his father with wide-eyed admiration.

"Please, not so loud," Mama said. "They'll hear you clear down at the newspaper office."

"Well, then, they'll know I'm coming." Papa looked at his gold watch. "I must go now or I'll be late for work. Come along, Rob."

"All right. Wait for me."

Mama called, "Don't be long, Rob. Come back home for your lesson."

Rob caught up with his father. "When did you learn to whistle, Papa?"

12

"When I was six years old just like you," his father said. "That was back in New England where I grew up. I kept trying and trying. Then suddenly one day I could whistle. I don't know how. I just stopped whooshing and really whistled." He looked down at the boy trotting along beside him. "It will happen to you, too. All of a sudden. You'll see."

Papa started whistling again. This time he whistled "The Cavaliers of Dixie," a marching tune about the South in the War between the States. Rob, trying to keep in step with his father, puckered his mouth and blew, too. Much to his disappointment, the only sound that came out was more whooshing.

The two of them walked several blocks to the newspaper office. They walked briskly along wooden sidewalks and across cobblestone streets, whistling and whooshing together.

It was a beautiful morning. The sea fog was

lifting. The California sun was beginning to burn bright. Specks of dust whirled up in the yellow light. Rob thought they looked like gold. Maybe the dust really was gold dust.

At last they came to the newspaper office. Mr. Frost stopped to read the headlines pasted in the window under the date: April 8, 1880.

"Nothing very exciting today," Papa said, "but I must get to work. Good-bye, son."

"Good-bye, Papa. Maybe when you come home tonight I'll know how to whistle like you."

Rob knew Mama expected him home for school. It wasn't a real school where he had to stay indoors all day. This was merely a pretend school. Often he just listened to a Bible story. Nobody could tell a story like Mama.

Rob kept on whooshing as he climbed back up the long hill to the yellowish houses in his own neighborhood. Each house had a bay window in front. "Like shining eyes," Rob thought.

14

Women along the way were sweeping their porches or steep front steps. One or two of them called "Good morning" to Rob as he passed. He stopped whooshing long enough to call back, "Good morning."

When he reached home, nobody was in sight. Nobody had swept off the Frost porch or was sweeping down the front steps. Rob knew that Mama wasn't much interested in sweeping. She liked books better than brooms.

"If you read a book," she said, "you can remember it always. But when you sweep a floor, you have to do it again the next day."

As Rob ran up the steps and in the front door, he could hear Jeanie's high sweet voice. She was only four, but she learned quickly. "Say it again, Mama," she begged, "that part from the book where it says,

'A hundred voices joined the shout
With hark and whoop and wild halloo.'"

15

Mama laughed. "Good lass," she said to Jeanie. "Here's Rob. He can help you dry the breakfast dishes. And I'll tell you more about the hunter on his horse, chasing the stag with those grand dogs of his."

Rob took a dish towel off the rack in the kitchen, and Jeanie still held a dish towel in her small hands. But Mama forgot all about washing the dishes in the tin dishpan. The water grew cold as she went on saying poetry from "The Lady of the Lake":

"Two dogs of black St. Hubert's breed
Unmatched for courage, breath, and speed."

Jeanie stood spellbound. Rob leaned against the sink, breathing hard. If only he had two dogs like that, he thought, then surely he could whistle them to his side. Together they could climb the highest mountain near San Francisco. Or any mountain in Scotland where Mama had come from long ago. Or even one of those

16

mountains in New England that Papa climbed when he was a boy. And if ever his dogs strayed from his heels, all he would have to do would be to whistle them back!

Mama's voice went on and on. Suddenly they heard a bell clanging outside and a voice calling, "Scissors? Scissors sharpened! Knives sharpened like new!"

Mama smoothed back her brown hair. She shook her head as though she were waking from a dream. "Oh, dear," she said. "There's the scissors grinder. Go stop him, Rob."

The grinder was a small, wiry man. He was bent over, carrying his grindstone between boards strapped on his back. Beside him trotted a small black dog. "Any scissors and knives today?" the man asked. "I grind cheap."

"Yes," Rob said. "Mama's getting things together for you."

The man swung his contraption off his back

and set it down on its three wooden legs. The dog came over to lick the boy's hand. Then Rob started to pat the dog and asked, "Can I watch you sharpen?"

"Yes. And you can help, too, if you want. What's your name?"

"Robert Lee Frost."

"How old are you?"

"I was six last month."

"Good. Here, fill this can with water. This old stone is thirsty."

Rob ran back into the kitchen to the pump by the sink and made a few quick pushes on the handle. He filled the tin can with water and carefully carried it out to the grinder.

Mama was there now, giving him her collection of kitchen knives, her big scissors, and the small scissors from her sewing basket. Then she went back to finish washing dishes.

The grinder gave the stone wheel its first spin,

letting Rob pour a little water on it. Then the man started working the foot pedal that made the stone turn round and round. For a long time he pedaled, holding the blades of the knives one at a time across the turning stone. Each one became shiny and sharp.

The man didn't talk much. Sometimes he nodded to Rob to drip more water on the stone to keep it from getting hot. The dog closed one eye, half dozing in the sunshine. The stone wheel made a buzzing, gritty sound as it turned.

"Sounds like mosquitoes," Rob thought. He started whooshing again under his breath, keeping time to the grindstone's tune. He whooshed louder and louder. The wheel whirred faster and faster. Finally the last knife and the last pair of scissors were sharpened.

"Watch my dog for me while I take these in to your mama," the grinder said. "If he wanders off, just whistle!" The man disappeared into the

Frosts' house before Rob could confess he didn't yet know how to whistle.

A yellow cat came out from the house next door and started down the steps. Before Rob could grab the dog's collar, the dog was off. He went like a streak across the board walk and up the steps. The cat fled inside the house, and someone slammed the door. Outside, the dog whined and pawed at the door.

Without thinking, Rob puckered his lips to whoosh at the dog. But instead of whooshing, he whistled! A real honest-to-goodness whistle came out. Just like that, it happened.

The whistle felt like one. It sounded like one. Even the dog knew it was a whistle, because he came trotting back to Rob's side.

"I can do it! I can do it!" Rob said happily. He knelt down and hugged the dog.

"Do what?" the grinder asked, as he came back, jingling change in his pockets.

Rob whistled again. He was still whistling when the grinder went off down the street ringing his bell. He whistled all day long. That night he greeted his father with his best whistle yet. This whistle wasn't so loud as the whistle on a steam locomotive, but Papa agreed it was an honest-to-goodness whistle. "It won't be long until you'll be whistling a real tune," he said, looking down with pride.

"Like the 'Cavaliers of Dixie'?" Rob asked. "I can't do that yet." Then he grinned. "But at least I won't be whooshing any more."

Once by
the Pacific

IN A FEW weeks Rob could whistle his father's favorite tune. He never grew tired of whistling this tune, but one day his mother clapped her hands over her ears and said, "Please whistle something else, Rob."

"But I don't know any other tune," Rob protested.

"Then I'll teach you one, a bonny Scotch song by Robert Burns. It's about a lake, Loch Lomond. This is the chorus:

'Oh you'll take the high road
And I'll take the low road,
And I'll be in Scotland before ye.' "

Mama sang and Rob whistled this old tune until he knew it by heart, too. It was a good song to whistle on the hilly streets of San Francisco. It was a good tune to whistle when the Frost family set out for a day at Cliff House.

"What's Cliff House?" Jeanie asked as her father lifted her up high to put her on a seat in the omnibus beside her mother.

Rob clambered up on the front seat by the driver so he could be near the horses. "Cliff House," he said, "is sort of a hotel by the ocean and best of all, it's near Seal Rocks!"

"What are Seal Rocks?" Jeanie asked.

"You'll see, we'll all see, Seal Rocks by the sea," Rob chanted.

The horse-drawn omnibus was soon filled with Papa's newspaper friends and their families. They all were in high spirits. What a sparkling day to go to the seashore!

The driver cracked his whip and slapped the

24

reins on the horses' backs. The horses were off at a fast walk, and their hooves clattered on the cobblestone streets. The passengers rode past white walls covered with honeysuckle and jasmine blossoms. Finally they reached the edge of the city, where the horses broke into a fast trot.

Rob whistled, "You'll take the high road, and I'll take the low road." All the time he pretended to be driving the horses himself. "Giddap," he said, snapping his pretend whip.

"When we get to Cliff House are we going swimming?" Rob asked Papa.

Mama spoke up. "No, the water will be too cold and the undertow too dangerous, but you may play on the beach."

Suddenly Rob called out, "There's the sea, I see the sea!" His keen eyes had caught a glimpse of sparkling blue water ahead.

In no time all the passengers piled out of the

25

omnibus by Cliff House. The men went into the club room, and the women walked out on the veranda overlooking the ocean. The children started down the steep hill toward the water.

Soon they heard strange roaring noises that sounded like huge dogs grown hoarse from barking. Jeanie clutched Rob's hand. "What's making those scary noises?"

"The seals," Rob explained. "Look at them out there on Seal Rocks."

"I don't see anything but big brown rocks," Jeanie said.

"Look again. See all those shiny brown things move on the rocks? Those are the seals. And listen to them bark!"

Just then one enormous seal took a sudden dive into the ocean. Others followed until the water was almost filled with sleek swimmers. They kept lifting their huge flippers out of the water and rolling into the waves.

On the rocks other seals were crawling up or down the steep and slippery sides, roaring hoarsely all the time. "Look at that one, high on the very top," Rob said. "See, he's taking a snooze in the sun. He's so big he must be king of them all."

Just then a bird, a sea gull, settled on the seal's head. The seal let out a bellow as loud as thunder. Away flew the gull, joining the other birds flying around in circles.

Everybody laughed. Rob started making loud noises deep in his throat. "I'm a seal!" he said. "Look, I'm a seal!" He pretended his arms were flippers and lifted them in turn, up and down through the air. He swayed from side to side through the sand, roaring all the time. Soon the other boys were roaring seals.

"I want to be a seal, too," Jeanie called.

Rob stopped for breath. "No, no," he said. "You girls can be sea gulls."

At once, Jeanie and a girl named Milly made their arms flap like wings. They darted in and out screaming among the bellowing boys.

Rob crawled up to the top of a flat rock on the beach. He lay down, closed his eyes, and pretended to nap. As quick as a sea gull, Jeanie climbed up and sat on Rob's head. Rob let out a roar that sent her giggling down to the sand.

"Children! Children!" Mrs. Frost was calling. "It's time for dinner. Come for dinner."

All the pretend seals and sea gulls turned quickly back into hungry boys and girls. "I'll race you to Cliff House," Rob called.

After a big fish dinner, Milly said, "Let's play croquet. I can beat anybody here."

The children rushed out on the croquet court where Milly took charge of the game. She handed out the mallets and wooden balls to the children. She told everybody how to play and what the rules were.

In the lively game that followed, Milly kept ahead of everybody else. Finally she had her ball where she could knock it through the last two wickets and win. Then it was Rob's turn, and he knocked his ball through a wicket so that it rolled fast and hard right at Milly's ball. Clunk! It hit!

Milly jumped up and down in protest. Her face was red with anger, even though she knew that Rob had made a good play. "Don't you dare to send my ball way off!" she cried. "Don't you dare!"

Rob grinned. "The rules say that I can if I want to, and I want to!" At once he sent Milly's ball clear to the other end of the court.

Before Rob could turn around, Milly rushed over to him. She raised her mallet high and brought it down *whack* on Rob's head. Rob cried out with pain and ran after Milly, but she ran toward Cliff House, calling, "Mama, Mama!"

When he caught up with her, she was clinging to her mother. "That boy's after me. Keep him away. Don't let him hit me!"

Rob's father caught Rob by the arm. "Shame on you," he said. "Where are your manners?"

Rob looked indignantly at his father. He rubbed the lump on his head. "But, but she . . ." he sputtered.

Papa wouldn't listen. "Don't tell tales now, and don't ever hit a girl."

Rob wrenched his arm away from his father and ran back outdoors. Then he kept on running down the hill and along the beach. He didn't care where he was going, just somewhere away from everybody.

Once he stooped to pick up a long piece of black seaweed. "It's like a whip," he thought, waving it in the air. "I wish I had a horse to run away with. We could go like the wind."

Finally he turned and began climbing up the rocky cliff. Out of breath, he flung himself down on a rock in a hollow between two higher rocks near the top.

"Grown-ups!" he muttered. "Fathers! They don't listen. They aren't fair. They always take sides with girls!" He felt the bump on his head, which seemed to be almost as big as an egg. He drew a long quivering breath. He closed his eyes and soon was fast asleep.

Later he opened his eyes and looked out over the ocean. Suddenly he realized the waves were high, higher than he had ever seen them before. He looked up at the dark sky. Black hairy looking clouds were scudding low over his head.

The wind was frightening. With a steady roar, it pushed the waves higher and higher and the clouds faster and lower. It pushed against the cliff, against his face.

Down below huge black waves rose like walls and crashed against the rocks. As Rob watched these waves, he had a dreadful thought. What if his family had gone off home and left him here? He was terrified. He thought, "What if the waves keep piling up higher and higher? What if they get so high they'll swallow me up?

They may swallow up the cliff, the land, and even the whole country!"

Rob buried his head in his arms. Suddenly he felt a hand on his shoulder. It was Papa saying, "I've been looking everywhere for you. What in the world are you doing out here all by yourself? Come on. Let's get back with the others. Stoop low, like this."

Crouching and crawling, Rob and his father made their way together back to the safety of Cliff House. In a few days the lump on Rob's head disappeared. He forgot all about this minor injury, but he never forgot his terror when he was caught alone in a storm by the Pacific.

A Strange Bird

ONE SUMMER when the wind started blowing sand over everything, Mrs. Frost said, "These sandstorms are terrible. It's impossible to keep a house clean during these sandstorms. Just look! I dusted this table once today. Now the sand dust is so thick you can write your name in it."

Rob decided to try it. Even though he was now eight years old, he did not know how to write much. But Mama had taught him how to write his own name. Now with his forefinger he traced his name on the table: Rob Frost.

Papa spoke up. "Write your full name, son.

You should be proud of it, after being named for a very great general."

"I am proud of it," Rob said. "But it's a pretty long name to write."

Papa snorted. "Why your name isn't long. What if you were saddled with the name of Ulysses Simpson Grant Frost?"

Rob grinned. Then carefully he wrote again. This time he put: Robert Lee Frost.

Jeanie jumped up and down. "Watch me. I can write my name, too." In large letters she printed: Jeanie Florence Frost.

With a flourish Papa signed his name: Wm. Prescott Frost.

Mama laughed. "I might as well add mine." In her careful schoolteacher's hand she wrote: Belle Moodie Frost. Then she said, "Now the table looks like a family record book instead of a place to eat. Once more I'll dust it off."

Papa coughed and said, "Back in New England people always said, 'Everyone must eat a peck of dirt before he dies.' Here they say, 'Eat a peck of gold.'"

"Is some of the dust really and truly gold?" Rob asked.

Papa laughed and said, "Of course it is." But Rob couldn't tell whether or not he was teasing.

Mama started setting the table. "Whatever it is, there is too much of it," she said. "The time has come for us to move for the summer. Papa can stay in a hotel here near his work. Your Aunt Blanche has found a good place for us in Napa Valley, where there are horses and chickens and lots of green growing things."

Rob liked the ride across the Bay in the big ferry boat. He liked riding in a farm wagon up through the green Napa Valley. He liked looking at the grapevines that stretched green and silver in the sun. And he liked Mr. and Mrs. Bragg with whom they were going to stay.

Rob's room was tiny, but he did not expect to spend much time there. Quickly he hung up his few extra clothes on the hooks behind a green curtain. Then he dashed downstairs and outdoors to explore.

First he watched the white chickens, pecking and clucking in the chicken yard. Then he ran to the pasture nearby and hung over the fence watching the horses. Maybe he could learn to ride while he was here!

One of the horses came trotting over to the fence. He nodded his head over the fence, blowing and whinnying at Rob. Rob picked a handful of grass and held it out to the horse.

The horse's big rubbery lips swept the grass out of Rob's hand. "I never knew a horse's mouth was so big," Rob thought. "He could swallow my hand in one bite if he wanted to."

But the horse didn't want to swallow Rob's hand. He just wanted to get more grass. His

37

lips tickled when Rob gave him another handful. Rob laughed.

"You seem to have a way with horses. Do you like to ride?" Mr. Bragg was coming up beside him with Mama and Jeanie close behind.

"Oh yes," Rob said. "I get along with horses very well."

Jeanie spoke up. "Why, Rob, what a story!" She looked up at Mr. Bragg. "He's always making up stories. Once he even told us an eagle tried to carry him away. And he's never been on a horse in his life!"

Mr. Bragg looked at Rob closely. "Well, sometimes I pretend things," Rob said. "Lots of times I play I'm riding a 'pretend' horse. And that is one of my favorite things to do."

Mr. Bragg laughed. "Well how about a real ride on a real horse? Billy here is gentle. You seem to be friends with him. I'll help you up, and you can ride him around the pasture."

Mr. Bragg boosted Rob up on Billy's bare back. For a minute Rob stretched out on his stomach, clinging to Billy's mane. He was afraid so far from the ground. What if he fell off?

Mr. Bragg said, "Sit up straight. You can still hold on."

Off they went at a slow walk. Rob's eyes were shining. The first time around the field he hardly dared look up or down or to right or left. Jeanie called out to him, "Is it fun?"

Rob nodded but didn't dare turn his head to look at her. The second time around he grinned happily at Mr. Bragg, Mama, and Jeanie. The third time around he slapped his bare heels against Billy's sides to make him go faster.

Rob let go of the mane and turned to wave to the three by the fence. Then all at once he fell off Billy to the ground. Kerplunk!

Mr. Bragg and the others ran over to him. Jeanie was crying. "Oh, maybe he's dead!"

"Nonsense," said Mr. Bragg. "He's just had the breath knocked out of him. You'll see."

Rob opened his eyes and smiled weakly. In a minute he was up and walking, good as new. "Falling off a real horse hurts more than falling off a 'pretend' horse," he said. "But riding a real horse is more fun than just pretending. Now let me ride Billy again."

Every day Rob rode Billy until he felt as much at home on horseback as he did on his own two feet. He never fell off again.

Chickens were Jeanie's favorite animals. When she came to scatter grain in the chicken yard, they came running. They fluttered all around her. Mrs. Bragg let Jeanie gather the eggs every day.

The first time Rob tried to help her, he squeezed an egg tight and it broke in his hand, leaving a sticky mess. "I'd rather eat eggs than gather them," he said.

Mr. Bragg told Rob that he could look after locking up the chicken house each night. One morning during breakfast, he told how the night before, a coyote, fox, or some such critter had tried to get into the chicken house. He had heard a tremendous squawking. He smiled at Rob. "Thanks to our young guard here, everything was locked up tight. And the chickens were safe from the prowler, whatever it was."

One evening Rob found a loose hinge on the door of the chicken house. He was tempted to let it go, but he couldn't bear to leave the chickens in danger. So, with hammer and nails, he fixed the hinge firmly in place.

Rob began to pretend. "What if some small creature like a bird should get into the chicken house? The bird wouldn't be hungry for chickens, but for eggs. What if the bird had a sharp bill, sharp as a nail! It could peck at the eggs, couldn't it, like this?"

Rob reached into a nest, pulled out an egg, and cradled it in one hand. With his other hand he reached into his pocket and pulled out a nail, sharp and shiny. Gingerly he tapped one end of the egg with the pointed nail. Nothing happened. Again he tried, and the nail made a neat round hole. Then he made a hole in the other end of the egg, too!

Rob held the egg up to see if any of the insides would drip out, but not a drop came out either end. He was glad because the Braggs would be upset if Jeanie brought messy eggs to the house. This way the family would just be puzzled by the odd holes in the egg.

Rob put the egg carefully back in the nest. Then he decided to poke holes in all the other eggs, one after another. He had just finished when Jeanie came into the chicken house, swinging her empty basket. "What are you doing in the chicken house?" she asked.

43

"Oh, I just nailed a loose hinge on the door to make everything safe."

"Good," Jeanie said. "We don't want a fox or weasel or coyote getting our chickens."

"Or strange birds either," Rob said with a straight face as he went out the door.

The next morning while Rob and the others ate their fruit, Mrs. Bragg called from the kitchen. "How do you want your eggs today? With bacon?"

Rob almost said, "No, with holes," but he just grinned and kept quiet.

Mama suggested scrambled eggs for everyone. Rob stopped eating his orange and listened. What was Mrs. Bragg muttering about?

Through the open door Rob could see her take one egg after another out of the basket. She looked at each one carefully. "That's queer," she was saying. "And here's another, and another. The strangest thing I ever saw!"

44

Rob giggled and quickly put his hand over his mouth. Mrs. Bragg came in and put the egg basket on the dining table. "Look here," she said. "There are tiny round holes in the ends of each egg. Every single one! How in the world do you suppose they ever got there!"

Mr. Bragg was as puzzled as everyone else. "I never saw the like in all my years of raising chickens," he said.

Rob asked, "Do you suppose it's some kind of critter? A snake maybe?" He giggled again but Jeanie shivered.

"No," Mr. Bragg said. "A snake would have swallowed the egg whole. It must be something with a beak, a small beak, but mighty sharp."

"Rob, did you fasten the door tight last night?" asked Mr. Bragg.

"Yes, sir," said Rob quickly.

"He even fixed a loose hinge, didn't you, Rob?" Jeanie spoke up, proud of her brother.

Rob's face grew a little red at this, but he managed to say "Yes," again.

Mrs. Bragg scrambled the eggs and everyone thought they were good. But all through breakfast, everyone tried to guess what could make the mysterious holes in the egg shells. Everyone agreed it must have been a strange bird. But what kind?

Rob was delighted with all the excitement. His eyes sparkled. Once he nearly choked from trying not to laugh.

After breakfast he ran outdoors for a gallop on Billy. "Nobody will ever know what kind of strange bird really made the holes in the eggs," he thought. "This bird was a plain old 'rob-in,' that's what it was. And I'm that old 'Rob-in.' "

Two Monkeys
and a Glass

WHEN SUMMER was over, the members of the Frost family were happy to be together again in San Francisco. One day Mama said to Rob, "Now that you are eight and a half years old, you are old enough to try going to a real school. Jeanie can go, too. School started a week ago, but I'm sure you can catch up."

Papa didn't seem to care whether Rob went to school or not. "But if you do go," he said, "work hard and mind your manners."

The next day Rob and Jeanie started off to school. They were late because they had to dress in new clothes. Rob wore a new brown suit. He didn't object, but it felt funny after going barefoot to wear shoes and stockings.

"These stockings make my legs itch," he said, leaning over to scratch his legs.

Jeanie in a blue dress and new red shoes held tight to Rob's hand as they went into the school. The primary teacher welcomed six-year-old Jeanie as a new pupil. Rob was told to go to a room for bigger boys and girls.

Rob's new shoes squeaked as he walked down the hall. For a long minute he stood outside the closed door, trying to get up courage to knock. He could hear a boy inside the room reading in a loud voice: "There was once a hen who lived in a farmyard, and she had a large brood of chickens." Rob grinned. He knew all about chickens—and their eggs.

The teacher in the room was a man, who soon came to the door. He stood and looked down at Rob. "Hello, there! Who are you?" he asked.

Remembering his manners, Rob spoke up. "My name is Robert Lee Frost, sir. I am supposed to start school today."

"All right, Robert Lee Frost," the teacher said. "Come in and start."

Rob was given a seat and a McGuffey reading book. All the boys and girls stared at him. "Suppose you stand up and read for us, Robert," said the teacher. "Begin with 'The Quarrelsome Cocks' on page 103." The teacher's finger pointed halfway down the page.

Rob took a deep breath and began to read. "Here is a story about two foolish cocks that were always—" Next was a strange word.

The teacher said, "The word is *quarreling*."

"Yes, sir, *quarreling*." Rob went on reading. "which is very—" Again he stopped.

Again the teacher helped him. "This time, the word is *naughty*."

"Yes, sir, *naughty*. You do not——"

"That will be enough, Robert," said the teacher. "Perhaps you are not ready for this reader. We'll see. Now you read, Milly."

In the front row, Milly stood up. She rattled off the words so fast that Rob lost his place in the book. As the day went on, he found out that most of the children could write, spell, and do arithmetic problems better than he could.

After school Rob was ashamed when he had to tell his mother and father that tomorrow he would be put back with the smaller children. Mama was comforting. "Never mind, lad. You will catch up fast if you work hard. You probably know more Bible stories and poems by Robert Burns than any boy in your room. And they're important."

Even Papa did not scold Rob about the reading lessons. "*Naugh-ty* cocks!" he snorted. "Cocks don't *quar-rel*. They fight. Some things you can learn better outside of school."

For awhile Rob kept on going to school in a lower grade. One day when he had a cold, his mother decided to keep him home for awhile. So he quit school, and his mother began to teach him at home.

Often in the morning Rob walked with his father to the newspaper office. Papa never said much on these walks along the city streets, but Rob enjoyed them. He liked to hear the clang, clang of the cable cars as they rolled up or down the hills past them.

One morning Rob asked why his father never rode to work. Papa answered, "Cable cars are all right for people who don't know how to walk. Why, once I was in a walking race that lasted six days. I almost won the race, too. I just lost by a hair's breadth.

"Remember," he went on, "walking was invented long before cable cars. Those cars weren't even running till the year before you were born. Come on, Rob, stretch your legs. You'll have to if you want to keep up with me."

Rob tried to take longer steps. He was glad when they stopped at a Chinese washhouse, where Papa had left a shirt to be laundered. Rob was always fascinated by the strange long robe the laundryman wore, and by his little round cap. He stared at the long black braid hanging down the man's back.

"Why do the Chinese wear pigtails like that?" he asked as they left the washhouse.

"That braid is called a queue," Papa said. "It seems to be part of the Chinese religion in some way. It's a badge of national honor, too. The worst thing you could ever do to a Chinaman would be to pull or cut his queue off. Don't ever try it."

At last Rob's father dashed up the steps of his newspaper office, and Rob rushed home for an hour's lesson with Mama. With her help he was beginning to read better, but he thought he never would be able to read as well as she could. She could make a poem sound as exciting as if she were telling a story.

Today at the end of the lesson Mama said, "Now go outdoors in the fresh air. Here's a sandwich to take with you. Be sure to be back when Papa comes home, so we can all eat supper together."

Rob often wished he had someone to run around with him, but all the boys his own age were in school. Today, as usual, he'd have to make his own fun.

Since Rob would have almost a full day, he decided to go to the zoo at Woodward's Gardens, some distance away. He wished he could ride the Mission street horsecar, but he had no money. Besides, Papa would say, "Stretch your legs, boy." So Rob started the long walk, whistling as he went.

At the zoo, Rob first stopped to look at a big eagle that sat blinking at him from a cage. He felt sorry for the eagle and thought of how strong the bird would be if he were free to fly over the mountains. "Why, he could even swoop down over a boy like me in the valley," Rob thought, "and carry me off in his fierce-looking claws!"

Rob sometimes pretended that an eagle almost carried him away. The very thought of it always made him shiver. He shivered now.

Suddenly he stopped, just in time to keep from stepping on something lying on the ground. It was a small round magnifying glass, sparkling in the sunlight. His father would call it a "burning glass."

Rob picked it up. He turned it this way and that, catching the rays of the sun. When he held it a certain way, he could see a tiny whole sun winking back at him from inside the glass. It would be fun to look at the animals through the glass. He decided to try it.

Before long Rob came to the monkeys' cage in the zoo. Two small monkeys came loping to the front of the cage. Each one hung by one purple-brown paw from a bar overhead. Each put a long hairy arm around the other monkey's shoulder.

They stared at Rob and his glass with their bright eyes. Rob thought the monkeys looked like comical but sad little boys, wearing brown masks for Halloween.

As Rob turned the glass in his hand, he found that the sun made a pinpoint of light bounce off the surface. Soon he tilted the glass and made a small bright spot of light shine on the first monkey's nose. Then he swung the dot of sunlight over to the nose of the other monkey. Both monkeys blinked and looked puzzled.

Rob made the spot of light dance back and

forth from one small flat nose to the other. One monkey uncurled his paw from around the bar in the cage to touch his nose. Then the light danced on his knuckles. The monkey looked more puzzled than ever.

Rob wondered whether the monkeys thought the stinging light was something they could pick off and throw away. He was certain they didn't understand anything about the glass. Carelessly, he took a step closer to the cage.

In a flash, one hairy brown arm reached out and snatched the glass from Rob's hand. Then, in great excitement, both monkeys swung back into the shadows of their cage to examine the mysterious prize.

One of them bit the glass. Did he think it was a strange sort of fruit? The other broke off the handle and pulled off the tortoise rim. Did he think it would peel like a banana? The monkeys still seemed to be puzzled.

Rob hoped the monkeys would bring the glass back to him. Instead they finally grew tired of it and hid it deep in their straw bedding. With empty paws they came swinging back to stare at Rob through the bars.

Rob couldn't help laughing. The little creatures looked more than ever like sad and comical little boys wearing Halloween masks.

"But," thought Rob, "real boys would know what to do with a burning glass. They would know how to bounce spots of light on my nose, but the monkeys don't know how. They don't even know enough to give my glass back to me."

Rob and
the Gang

SOMETIMES Rob saw big boys roaming the streets of San Francisco. They didn't go to school or seem to have anything to do. "They're hoodlums," Papa said. "Better leave them alone."

As the boys wandered about, they seemed to have a lot of fun together. They never paid any attention to Rob until he was ten years old. Then one day when he was down by the seawall, he suddenly got mixed up with them.

A half dozen big boys were leaning over the wall, watching the busy harbor. They didn't even notice Rob leaning against the wall.

Rob always enjoyed the sights and smells of the waterfront. Today waves were slapping against the black wooden piles that held up the docks. Men were shouting orders to others unloading cargo from vessels tied up alongside. They rolled and hauled and heaved barrels and bales of freight from the boats onto wagons. Hitched to each wagon were huge dray horses stamping their feet.

The big boys were guessing what was in the different loads being taken from the ships. "There's cotton in those bales," one said.

"There's coffee beans in the bags," said another. "You can smell the coffee."

Rob sniffed with delight. Yes, he was sure the bags contained coffee, but he didn't dare say so. The boys didn't even look at him.

"What's in those barrels?" asked the biggest boy, the one they called Balso. He pointed to a wagon almost loaded and ready to go.

"Probably diamonds from Africa," guessed a boy named Frank.

"Nah! Diamonds don't come in barrels," Balso said. "More likely they're fancy dishes from China for some posh place here in the city like the Palace Hotel."

Rob's keen eyes caught sight of some brown grainy stuff trickling through a crack in the barrel. "Sugar!" he said in a loud voice.

The boys looked at him for the first time. "Nah!" Balso said again. "I bet it's rum!"

The driver of the wagon, which was piled high with the barrels, soon cracked his whip. The horses started off, straining to pull their heavy load. All the boys turned to watch the wagon. They saw it reach the end of the dock and lurch onto the cobblestone street. Next, much to their delight, they noticed that the top barrel at the back of the load was loose.

Suddenly the barrel rolled off the wagon and

fell with a crash on the street. Out spilled its contents, piling up in high brown hills, sparkling in the sun. "Sugar!" the boys shouted. "The kid's right. It's sugar. Come on!"

Rob ran with the rest. Never had he seen such mountains of sweetness. With whoops of joy the boys plunged their hands into the brown sugar. They scooped up the sweet stuff, filling their mouths, pockets, and even their shirts.

The boys scrambled and shoved. Soon they had sugar in their hair, in their noses, in their ears. Then they began throwing sugar at each other. Rob threw with the rest.

In the midst of the scrambling, Rob looked up and saw the driver coming back, brandishing his whip. "Look out!" Rob called. "Better run!"

Balso, with Rob at his heels, led the bunch down the street. Rob ran faster than he had ever run in his life. The driver took out after them. Balso, Rob, and the others ducked behind a big warehouse. The driver saw them peeking from behind the building and shook his fist in their direction. Then he went back to his broken sugar barrel.

The boys pounded each other gleefully on the back. They pounded Rob, too. "You can run fast," Balso said to Rob. "When you run with us you've got to be fast and ready for anything that happens. That sugar fight was a dandy!"

Rob grinned as he tried to shake the sugar out of his hair. "It was the sweetest fight I was ever in," he said.

The boys laughed. Then Balso said, "If you stick with us, you'll have to do what I say, because I'm the boss. I'm the cock of the walk, and we don't want any chickens."

"I'm no chicken," Rob said. "That driver with his whip didn't scare me one bit."

"Him? He was nothing. Wait till you get in a real fix. Then we'll see what you do."

Rob was pleased to have new friends to run around with. He didn't dare tell his parents about Balso's gang. They'd be sure to forbid his having anything to do with them. "Hoodlums" they would be certain to call them.

And Rob didn't tell the gang anything about his lessons at home with Mama. "Sissy" they'd call him, or worse. Some days after his lessons, Rob didn't even see the boys. Other days he ran into them down on the waterfront. Or he saw them jumping off a cable car after hitching a free ride.

So far they let Rob tag along whenever he wanted to. So far Balso hadn't ordered him to do anything he was scared to do, but he never knew what was coming next.

One of the gang's favorite sports was annoying the Chinese. Balso and Frank even pulled their queues, then ran. Rob hoped Balso wouldn't order him to jerk a long black braid.

He didn't want to tease the Chinese, but he now was too afraid of Balso to refuse.

One day Rob went with the gang to an apricot orchard outside the city. It was a wonderful place! There was so much fruit left on the ground that the boys soon filled their pockets with the sweet golden fruit!

The next day the boys went back to the orchard, taking a large burlap bag. On the way Balso said to Rob, "When the ranchers go in to have their dinner, you shinny up the tree and pick some of the best apricots. Throw them down to us. We'll fill the bag."

When they reached the empty orchard at the noon hour, they found there were only a few apricots left. All of them had been picked from the trees. The only ones left on the ground had been bruised and stepped on.

Rob was secretly relieved, but Balso, Frank, and the others were disgusted. "All this walk for nothing," they said. "Well, we gotta find something to put in the bag." Balso added, "Look sharp now on the way home."

Rob enjoyed the walk home. He enjoyed the sunshine on the white walls, the bright flowers in every garden, the birds singing. All the while he knew that these weren't the kinds of things Balso was after.

Suddenly the air was filled with the squealing of pigs. The noise came from behind a wall where animals were being butchered in a slaughter house. Balso caught Rob by the arm. "Go get us a pig!"

Rob hesitated. He was afraid to climb over the wall. But he was even more afraid to tell Balso he was scared. Balso gave him a push. "Get going," he said. "Here's the bag and come back with a pig!"

With that, Rob found himself climbing over the wall. His heart began to pound as he

66

dropped down inside a big yard. Two men were herding a mass of squealing pigs into a pen next to the slaughter house. Luckily for Rob, the men had their backs to him.

Quick as a wink, Rob grabbed a small pig that was running away from the rest. He pushed the squirming, squealing pig into the burlap bag. The other pigs were making such a racket that nobody heard the one squealing pig that had vanished. Frank leaned over the wall and took the wriggling bag from Rob.

When Rob himself got back over the wall, Balso and the boys were already running down the street. Rob ran, too, looking back over his shoulder from time to time. The men weren't running after him.

Balso headed right for Chinatown. This time he didn't want anybody to pull a queue. Instead, he sold the pig to a Chinese cook for 90 cents. "Here's your share," he said, handing Rob

15 cents. "You did a good job for us, and we can use you again."

Rob was so glad the whole adventure was over, that he didn't care whether he got anything. Most of all he was happy that nobody guessed how scared he had been.

Balso said, "Come on out tonight. We have a lot more fun after dark."

Rob swallowed hard. He knew his parents would never let him go out alone at night, but he didn't want to admit it. "I think I've got to go somewhere with my father tonight," he said, "but I'll see you soon."

As Rob headed toward home, he worried about what his parents would do if they knew what he had been doing. Mama would look sad. Maybe she would even pray for him. Papa might whip him, as had happened before.

When he reached home, how quiet and peaceful it seemed! Jeanie had her nose in a book as usual. Papa hadn't come home. Mama was writing at the dining table with a book open beside her.

"Ah, lad," she greeted Rob absently. "Are you hungry? I won't start supper until I finish writing this book review for Papa's paper. Why don't you help yourself to a peach or apricot or something?"

Mama turned back to her writing. She wasn't going to ask him any questions about his day, thank goodness.

And when Papa came home that night, he was so full of politics that he asked Rob only one question, "How would you like to go to a political meeting with me tonight? It's high time you learn the ins and outs of politics."

Into Politics

AT THE SUPPER table Rob was glad to see Papa in a good mood. He didn't act cross even though his supper was late. He scolded Rob only once when Rob forgot and put his elbows on the table. He read Mama's book review and said his newspaper would be glad to print it.

Papa liked politics and was in high spirits this evening because he was going to a political rally. And tomorrow he was going to the Democratic National Convention in Chicago.

"Are Mama and Jeanie going to the meeting with us tonight?" Rob asked his father.

"No, of course not," Papa answered. "Politics

are not for ladies. They're for men like us." He laughed and clapped Rob on the shoulder.

"At election time you'll be sorry women aren't allowed to vote, especially since you are going to run for Tax Collector," Mama teased. "I might even decide to vote for you."

Rob spoke up. "I'd vote for you Papa, if I were old enough."

"Thank you, son. Let's see. How long will it be before you can vote?"

"Well," Rob said. "I'm ten years old now. So it will be eleven more years before I am twenty-one and can vote."

"Well, you're old enough right now to start learning about politics," Papa said. "Maybe you're even old enough to help me in my campaign. We'll see about that later."

Rob was delighted at the idea. He was delighted, too, to go out after dark with his father. Mama made him promise to stay close to Papa.

72

"San Francisco is a rough place at night. You shouldn't be out alone here."

The city looked magical to Rob at night. The summer stars were shining more brightly than he had ever seen them. The gas lamps on street corners glowed like a thousand candles.

The main streets were crowded with men. Many of them were going to the meeting at Pratt's Hall. Two big bonfires flamed high in front of the big hall. Rob threw back his head to watch the sparks fly upward. He wondered if they could fly as high as the stars.

Once he caught a glimpse of Balso and the boys moving quickly past the bonfires and down a dark alley. Whatever they were up to tonight, Rob was glad he wasn't with them. He still felt bad about swiping that pig. Besides, he felt more grown up to be with Papa and all his friends at the meeting.

Rob kept close to his father's heels as they

73

made their way inside the hall. When they reached the front row, Papa introduced Rob to his friend, Colonel Boyd, then to John Fogarty, County Chairman of the Democratic Committee. Papa was City Chairman.

"Here's a new young campaigner," Papa said. "He's going to help us elect the right people."

"Starting with the Tax Collector, eh?" Mr. Fogarty said. "Fine! We need all the help we can get!" He turned to Rob's father. "Don't forget, we're counting on you to make a rousing speech for Grover Cleveland."

On the platform, Mr. Fogarty pounded with his gavel for quiet. He called on one man after another to come up and speak. Rob grew restless waiting for his father to be called on. He tried hard to pay attention, but the speeches were long. They were about things he didn't understand at all. He heard over and over such words as "railroad monopoly," "tariff," "civil service reform," and "President Arthur." Everybody argued.

Rob slumped lower and lower in his seat. He yawned a big wide-open yawn. Papa poked him hard in the ribs. Rob swallowed the last of the yawn in a hurry. He sat up straight.

Within a few minutes he began to feel drowsy again. His eyelids drooped lower and lower. The speakers' long words grew fainter and fainter in his ears: "foreign trade," "gold reserve," "James G. Blaine."

Rob's head began to nod. Soon he went sound asleep. When he slumped over against his father, Papa poked him again. "Wake up," he whispered. "Where are your manners?"

Soon Chairman Fogarty said, "The last speaker is William P. Frost, our candidate for Tax Collector of the great city of San Francisco. He also is Delegate to the National Democratic Convention in Chicago!"

Rob sat up straight, wide awake now. He watched with pride as his father ran up the half dozen steps to the platform and strode to the speaker's stand. The Phi Beta Kappa key from Harvard, which his father always wore on his watch chain, shone in the lamplight.

Mr. Frost was not a good speaker, but he was confident. He stood straight and tall and his voice was clear. Best of all, Rob could understand what he was saying.

Papa ended his speech with an appeal to all California Democrats to stop arguing with each other. He said, "Let us remember that since before the War between the States our party hasn't had a single president in the White House. In this year of 1884, let us unite to work for that great Democrat who can become president. I pledge myself to work for his nomination in Chicago. That man is Grover Cleveland!"

Rob joined in the applause that rose like a

great ocean wave. He clapped until his hands ached. On the way home he said to his father, "I'm for Grover Cleveland for President and you for Tax Collector!"

Papa laughed. "Good! If I'm elected, that will be just the first step for me. Who knows where I might go in politics? Mayor of San Francisco? Congressman? Senator? But first of all we have to get Cleveland nominated in Chicago. Then you can start working for us both."

After his father left for Chicago, Rob ran several times each day to the newspaper office. At last the news came by telegraph. It was posted up in the window. "Democrats nominate Cleveland on second ballot."

Rob ran all the way home to tell Mama and Jeanie the good news. In the fall election it would be Grover Cleveland against James G. Blaine for President. "Let me go over to Oakland to meet Papa's train," Rob begged.

"Me, too," said Jeanie, jumping up and down. "We'll get to ride across on the ferry."

Mama smiled. "We'll all go and give him a real welcome."

Papa was eager to see his family and swung down off the steps of his car even before the train came to a stop. He doffed his tall hat when he greeted Mama. He gave Jeanie a big hug. Then he shook hands with Rob as though Rob were grown up.

Papa looked tired but pleased. "Well, son, so far so good. But we have a lot of work to do before we can elect Cleveland in November."

"And elect you, too, Papa, don't forget!" Rob said proudly.

Papa laughed. "I won't forget, not for a minute. You can start the first thing tomorrow, checking voter lists."

From the next day until election day, Rob was busy almost every minute. He was far too busy to spend any time with Balso and the boys. He ran on errands to City Hall for his father who had to work most of the time in his office.

Rob climbed up steps to hundreds of front doors and rang hundreds of doorbells. "Good morning, ma'am," he would say politely. "I have been sent to ask whether the man at this house is registered so he can vote in November."

At the answer Rob would check off a name on his list. Then he would smile and say, "Would you mind telling me whether your husband is a Democrat or Republican?"

Sometimes the lady would say, "I don't know," and sometimes she would say, "He is neither one. He belongs to the Greenback Labor Party." Sometimes she would say, "It's none of your business," and slam the door.

Most often the lady would smile at this boy with his eager blue eyes and grown-up manners. If she said, "My husband is for James G. Blaine.

He's a Republican," Rob's face would cloud over. Then he would make an "R" on his list.

If the lady said, "My husband is a Democrat. He's for Cleveland," Rob's face would light up like the sun over the Golden Gate! He would make a big "D" for Democrat on his list.

No matter what the lady said, Rob always reached in his pocket and pulled out a small white card. "See, it says 'Wm. P. Frost for Tax Collector, San Francisco.' Please give it to your husband when he comes home from work. And ask him to vote for Mr. Frost. He's my father."

"I will," the lady would say. Rob could only hope she would keep her promise.

By the end of the summer the lists were nearly complete. Rob was discouraged. "There are many more Republicans than Democrats on the lists," he said to Papa.

"I know," Papa answered, "but I think many independent Republicans or Mugwumps will vote for Cleveland instead of for Blaine. They think Cleveland is the better man."

"He's bigger, too," Rob said. Then he laughed as he looked up at the poster picture of Cleveland tacked up on the wall of Papa's office. "He must weigh a ton."

"No, only about two hundred and fifty pounds, but he will be the biggest President we have ever had."

Rob grinned. "Well, he looks like a big happy sea lion with his long moustache drooping down over his fat cheeks. Can he roar like one?"

"He can when he wants to," Papa said, "but he is absolutely honest and that's what counts. Come on, it's time to go to lunch. Maybe you can pass out some more of my cards there."

Out of Politics

PAPA's political friends welcomed him and Rob at the restaurant. There was much talking and laughing and arguing during the lunch. "How about having some of the pickled pigs' feet?" Papa asked Rob.

Rob made a face and said, "No, thank you." He didn't like to be reminded of pigs. Instead, he made himself a bologna sandwich with two big slabs of dark bread. He reached into the briny jar and fished out a big dill pickle. Then he helped himself to a peeled hardboiled egg, which immediately slipped through his fingers and rolled to the floor.

Rob looked fearfully at his father, but Papa just said, "No matter. Help yourself to another egg, boy. This time hold on to it."

Rob put his extra egg on a thick white plate with his sandwich. With great care he carried it to a small empty table near the wall. Papa stayed with his friends.

As Rob sat there eating he thought, "If I'd dropped that egg at home, Papa would have boxed my ears and sent me from the table without any dinner. How different he is when he's here having a good time with his friends like Colonel Boyd and Boss Buckley!

"It's because he's in politics and hoping to win that makes him so happy. I don't think he could stand losing the election. He just has to win when the ballots are counted. And I have to do more to help him!"

Rob looked around, wondering how. At one time or another he had handed Papa's card to every man there. He knew that Papa's friends would vote for him anyway, but he was afraid of what strangers might do. They might just stick his cards in their pockets and forget all about Wm. P. Frost for Tax Collector.

People wouldn't forget Grover Cleveland for President. His enormous poster picture was tacked up on one side of the restaurant. On the other side was a big picture of James G. Blaine for President. All the walls were crowded with smaller pictures and cards of persons who wanted to be elected to something.

Today Rob couldn't see his father's small card and wondered what had happened to it. He went over to the spot where he had tacked it up several weeks before. He found that it was still there but was almost hidden in the jumble of other cards on the wall.

Rob reached up and pulled off the card with its tack. He looked around for a better spot to put the card. There was hardly an inch of space left on any wall. About the only place left was the ceiling.

Rob grinned. If only he could climb like the monkeys in Woodward's Gardens! It would be grand to stick Papa's card up on the ceiling. Then people would pay attention! Then they would remember "Wm. P. Frost, Tax Collector."

He wondered whether there was any way to get the card up there. On impulse he threw it with its tack as hard and as high as he could. It sailed across the room and almost touched the ceiling. Then it fluttered down as light as a sea gull's feather. Finally it landed right in a bowl of shiny hardboiled eggs.

"Hey, there," cried the waiter. "What are you trying to do, boy?"

Everyone in the room looked at Rob. Papa took a step toward him. What if Papa boxed his ears right in front of everybody?

86

Rob took a deep breath and said, "I was just trying to tack my father's card up on the ceiling where people could see it."

When the men burst into laughter, Papa did, too. The men slapped Mr. Frost on the back. "Quite a campaigner you have there. We need more like him in the Democratic Party. He's got the spirit all right."

Papa's friend, Colonel Boyd, fished the card and tack out of the bowl. "Here, have another try, Rob," he said, "but don't try to throw the card like a baseball. And you can't drive the tack into the ceiling without some sort of weight behind it."

He reached into his pocket and pulled out a shining silver dollar. "How about this? If you can drive the tack up there, using this, the dollar is yours to keep."

Rob looked at his father who nodded. Colonel Boyd put the silver piece in Rob's open hand.

Then on top of the silver dollar Rob put the card with the tack sticking through it.

The waiter called, "Make sure the tack and card don't land in the dill pickle jar, but let

the silver dollar fall in, if you want to. I'll be glad to fish that out for myself."

Rob scarcely heard the waiter. He didn't listen either to the men who gathered around him, giving advice. He was figuring out the best way to throw the card and tack. The thing to do was to hurl them straight up.

Rob stole a quick glance at Papa who was looking proud and anxious. He put the silver dollar in the palm of his right hand and held the card on top with his hand so that the tack stuck upward. Then he swung his hand out in front of him, palm up, and let fly as hard as he could.

Up went the silver dollar, carrying the card and tack straight to the ceiling. In went the sharp tack, like an arrow pinning the card on target. Down fell the silver dollar, clinking and rolling on the floor.

The men cheered. Rob flushed with pleasure. "I was lucky," he said.

Papa picked up the dollar from the floor and gave it to Rob. "That was a perfect shot, son," he said. "Now what do you plan to buy with your silver dollar? More soda pop?"

Rob smiled. "No, sir, I think I'll keep it. Maybe I can use it to tack more of your cards on the ceiling."

Mr. Frost said, "That's a fine idea. There are other good ceilings all over town. Why don't we try some of them?"

The last week before election, Mr. Frost and Rob worked harder than ever. Mr. Frost made speeches. He wrote articles for Cleveland and the whole Democratic Party in California. Rob hurled Papa's cards at many ceilings in the city. In some places men didn't seem to care whether he tacked Papa's cards on the ceiling or not. All this was discouraging.

The day before election, Mama said to Rob, "Jeanie and I hardly see you any more. You are out from early morning until late at night. I'll be glad when this election is over."

"Well, it will be over tomorrow," Papa said. "I must admit I'll be glad, too. Campaigning for Democrats here is uphill work. If Cleveland doesn't win, I won't win either."

"But we've got to win!" Rob protested. "You and Cleveland are the two best men."

"That's the spirit," Papa said, "but the best men don't always win. I'll tell you what, though, Rob. If we win, I'll take you to Washington next March to see Cleveland inaugurated. How would you like that?"

Rob jumped up from the table in his excitement. "I certainly would. That would be the best thing that ever happened to me. Can we sit on the platform with Cleveland?"

Papa smiled. "I'm afraid not. Only important people will be invited to sit on the platform with him, but since we're loyal workers, we'd surely get to meet him. He would be especially pleased if we travel all the way from California to help him celebrate."

"Take me, too," Jeanie begged.

Papa shook his head. "No, but Mama can take you downtown tonight. You can watch for Rob and me in the big night-before-election parade."

That night San Francisco never grew dark. When the blaze of the sun died beyond the Golden Gate, other lights sprang to life in the city. Gas lights glowed, bonfires burned bright, Chinese lanterns bobbed in the breeze. Flaming torches were carried high in the two parades.

The Republicans marched first, chanting, "We want Blaine, the man from Maine!" Along the street Democrats shouted defiantly.

When the Democrats marched, Rob was one of the busiest persons in the parade. He rode, he walked, he ran, he shouted. He waved a sign which he had tacked onto Mama's old broomstick. On one side it said, "Grover Cleveland, the Honest Man." On the other side, it said, "Frost for Tax Collecter." Nobody bothered to tell Rob that he had spelled "collector" wrong.

First Rob rode with one of the volunteer fire companies on the hook-and-ladder wagon. Then he clambered up beside the driver on the steam-pumper fire engine. Finally he climbed down and ran up to the very front of the parade where Papa was marching. Papa gave him a flaming torch to carry with the torch bearers.

When the parade swept around the circle of the courtyard of the Palace Hotel, Rob heard his name called. Jeanie and Mama were leaning over one of the balconies, clapping hard. Rob waved his torch and shouted, "Cleveland for President! Frost for Tax Collector!"

It was after midnight before Rob fell into bed. He was worn out from all the excitement. But this was the last day of campaigning.

Next evening the election was over, but counting the votes went on for days. The election was close, so close that results were slow coming in. Rob and Papa couldn't bear to leave the newspaper office where the results kept coming in by telegraph.

Good news came from the East and the South. Rob cheered with Papa and the other men. Cleveland carried enough states to be elected whether he won California or not.

The news from San Francisco and all of California was bad for Democrats. Rob's father suddenly looked white and sick. Rob could tell from looking at him that he had lost. He tried hard to think of something to say.

Mr. Frost said, "Well, I told you, son, that you were old enough to learn the ins and outs of politics. It seems that you've learned more about the outs than anything else. Cleveland's in, but I'm out."

Rob winked back the tears. He remembered how happy his father had been a few weeks before when he had said, "If I win this time, who knows where I may go in politics."

Now Rob said timidly, "Maybe we'll have better luck next time, Papa."

"There won't be a next time," Papa said. "I can't go through all this campaigning again. Run home and break the news to Mama and Jeanie. Tell Mama I don't know when I'll be home."

Rob turned and ran out of the office. When he told Mama and Jeanie that Papa had lost, they cried. Rob cried, too.

The Big Race

"PAPA IS sick and there's nothing for me to do!" Rob thought one afternoon, as he sat on the top step of the front porch.

It was inauguration day, March 4, 1885. Long before Rob had given up hope of going to Washington to celebrate Cleveland's becoming President. Papa wasn't well enough and today he hadn't even gone to work.

Mama was worried about Papa. "You haven't really been well since you took part in that six-day walking race years ago."

With a flash of his old spirit, Papa answered, "I didn't lose that race by very much. I stayed in it till the end." Then with a sigh he added, "Now I think even Rob could beat me in a race."

Out on the steps Rob thought about how his father had changed. There had been no more good times together since the election.

Suddenly Rob's thoughts were broken by the sound of feet clattering on the wooden walk. He looked up and saw a group of boys coming around the corner, including Balso, Frank, and some of the old gang. All winter Rob had avoided them. Now here they were, stopping right in front of his house. How was he going to get rid of them?

"Hullo," Balso said. "So this is where you've been hiding."

"I haven't been hiding," replied Rob. "This is where I live."

Frank spoke up. "Well, why don't you run around with us any more? I bet it's because you can't keep up with us."

"I can run as fast as you can," Rob said.

"For a short distance, once around the block, maybe," Frank said. "But what about twice around? Or five times? Can you do that?"

Rob got to his feet. "Yes," he said. "I can beat you running ten times around."

Balso spoke up, egging him on. "What about twenty times? You're just a kid. I'll bet you can't last that long against Frank."

"I'll bet I can," Rob answered, running down the steps.

"All right, prove it," Frank said. "I dare you, I double dare you! Twenty times around the block for you against me."

"I'm ready whenever you are." Rob jumped up and down in his eagerness. He was scared to run against Frank, but he was excited, too. If only he could win! That would show everyone.

Balso took charge and led the boys to a vacant lot on a big hill. Rob and the gang scrambled

up the mound after Balso. "Here's the starting line," he said, making a mark in the dirt with a stone. "It's the finish line, too. Run up the Washington Street side first; then all around. No cutting corners!"

"All right," Rob said. "Twenty times around for both of us. Who's going to keep count?"

"I'll keep count," Balso said.

Rob didn't like this idea. Luckily he saw Jeanie just coming home from school. "Hey, Jeanie! Come up here and keep count for me. We're going to race around the block twenty times!"

Balso protested. "Aw, girls can't count straight."

"My sister can. She's good at school work like arithmetic. You and she can keep track for both of us. Then there won't be any mistakes."

Frank and Balso agreed. "No cheating, either. No monkeyshines!" Frank added, "Besides,

100

since you're smaller than me, you'll probably have to drop out way before we get to twenty."

Rob said only, "We'll see about that."

By now a few of the neighborhood boys, who had returned from school, were gathering near. They clapped Rob on the back saying, "We hope you beat that big fellow."

Balso yelled, "Ready! Get on your mark." Rob and Frank each toed his line.

"Get set." Each racer leaned forward.

"Go!" Each one was off like a shot.

The first ten times around were easy. Frank set a fast and steady pace. After a rather breathless start, Rob settled into the smooth stride he had learned long ago. So far, he and Frank kept rounding their corners and crossing the line at exactly the same moment. "Ten," Balso and Jeanie called out together.

"Keep going, Rob. You've reached the halfway mark," the neighbor boys yelled.

Frank's friends shouted at him, too. Everybody cheered every time Rob and Frank came into sight, and dashed past.

"Fifteen!" called Balso for Frank.

"Fifteen!" called Jeanie a few seconds later.

Rob was falling behind. He was breathing hard. Washington Street seemed steeper and steeper. He thought, "I must keep going!"

"Sixteen!" Balso shouted.

Later Jeanie called "Sixteen! Run, Rob!"

By now Rob felt as though his lungs would burst. He had lost count. He didn't even hear "Seventeen" or "Eighteen." All he knew was that Frank was ahead, always ahead now.

"Nineteen," yelled Balso. Up ahead, Frank disappeared around the corner on his last lap.

"Nineteen!" screamed Jeanie. Rob, way behind now, pounded doggedly past her.

"Last time around," all the boys yelled.

"Only one more to go," Rob thought.

"Twenty!" shouted Balso in triumph, as Frank reached the finish line.

"Twenty!" screamed Jeanie, as Rob fell in a heap over the line, gasping for breath.

Fully a minute passed before Rob could understand anything in the hub-bub of voices around him. Finally he managed to distinguish Frank, who was saying, "Well, I said you couldn't beat me and you didn't. But you stayed in the race till the end. I didn't think you could even do that much."

Rob could only grin weakly.

Balso said, "Any time you want to, you can run around with our gang. We'll see you soon." Then the boys trotted off down the street.

At home Rob's father said, "You didn't lose that race by much. You're a chip off the old block. When your legs get a little longer, you'll show 'em."

Rob had never been so tired or so happy as

he was that night. Just before he went to sleep, he thought, "I'm not afraid of Balso and Frank anymore! I don't have to do everything they tell me to if I don't want to, such as swiping pigs." Rob sighed with contentment. "And I'll race them around the block anytime, only the next time I'll make it twenty-five times!"

Before Rob saw the gang again, the Frosts moved across the Golden Gate for the spring and summer. Rob was delighted to help Papa put up a tent by the shore. The family was going to camp by the fishing village of Sausalito.

Mama hoped the fresh air would help Papa get well again. "Besides," she said cheerfully, "it will be a healthy place for the children to live during the summer."

"Yes, I'm glad," Jeanie said.

"As for me," said Papa, "I'll go swimming every evening after I come home on the ferry. What will you do with yourself, Rob?"

Rob sighed with pleasure. "Everything!"

And Rob did just about everything. Waking early, he ran down to see the fishing boats as they left the wharves before the sun came up. He watched them as they glided through the rosy mists past Angel Island. He watched the sea gulls dipping and wheeling over the water. He heard the waves clapping against the wharf.

After breakfast every day he climbed the hills that rose high behind the village. He scrambled down into deep flowered ravines. He wandered into the shadowed redwood forest, gazing up among the enormous trees. He thought their trunks soared like ship masts, and their tops surely scraped the sky.

Every afternoon, wherever Rob wandered, he planned to get back in time to meet Papa on the ferry. Each time he waited he worried about what Papa was going to be like. Only once had Papa seemed his old self, well and cheerful.

That was the time when he brought some of his Bohemian Club friends over with him.

"We'll have an evening of high jinks," Papa said laughing. Rob stayed up late to watch the fun and feasting around the bonfire.

But Mama stayed in the tent, keeping Jeanie with her. She shook her head when Rob urged her to come out. "Your father is a sick man," she said sadly. "I can't bear to watch him overdoing in this way."

One afternoon Rob went down to meet his father as usual. He watched the huge turtle-like ferry crawl and bump into its landing place. When he saw Papa, he was scared. Papa looked worse, but he insisted on going swimming.

Rob was not yet an expert swimmer like his father, so he stayed in shallow water. Papa swam past the piers out into the deep water of the bay, but today more slowly than usual. Rob watched anxiously and found it harder and harder to keep his father in sight. Finally he was just a black speck, disappearing between the waves far from shore.

Rob shivered with fear. What if Papa weren't strong enough to keep swimming? What if he should drown? Just before Rob turned to run for help, he again caught sight of the black speck, now coming back. He watched the speck come nearer and nearer, grow larger and larger.

Rob did not take his eyes off his father, even when he began floundering safely in shallow water. He waded out to help Papa back to shore where he sank on the sand, choking and gasping for breath.

Rob stood over his father, still shivering with fright. This time Papa was back safe from swimming. But Rob knew now that he would never be his old self again.

A Giant Stride

Early in May Rob's father died and was buried in New England. He had asked to be buried near his parents' old home north of Boston. "The Frosts belong in New England after all," he had said before he died.

Now, after the funeral, Rob and Jeanie and Mama stayed on in Grandmother and Grandfather Frost's big house in Lawrence, Massachusetts. Mama had no money to take the family anywhere else.

Night after night Rob lay awake in the big four-poster bed. He tried not to think much about Papa, but he couldn't help thinking about how far they were from home. His world had changed and New England seemed very different, very strange.

One night Rob thought, "It's just as if I were a giant. I crossed the whole continent in a single step. First I had both feet on the western shore by the Pacific Ocean. Then I took a giant-size step. Now here I am on the eastern shore, only twenty miles from the Atlantic Ocean, with both feet here.

"Of course," he admitted to himself, "I really came here by train. It took us several days and nights to get here. If I were a real honest-to-goodness giant, I could step right back to the Pacific coast again."

Rob sighed. He was homesick for the blue Pacific. He missed the hills of San Francisco all dusted with gold. "Here," he thought, "everything is gray. The whole town of Lawrence is gray with smoke from the cotton and woolen mills. Even Grandma's house is gray with thick curtains at all the windows.

"And Grandpa has a gray beard! He's the one who seems like a giant—a stern giant. He hardly ever scolds the way Papa did, but he never asks me to go walking with him to his mill. He never laughs as Papa did, and he never whistles. It's so quiet and polite around here I don't dare whistle myself. And Jeanie creeps around like a little mouse."

Rob punched his pillow, wishing he could go to sleep and forget everything. If it weren't for Mama, he didn't think he could stand it here in this stiff and proper house. When Mama and the children could be alone in their rooms, Mama still read to them.

As Rob stared into the dark with wide open eyes, he saw the door swing open. There stood Mama, holding a small oil lamp. The light through its clear glass chimney made the gold

110

of her earrings gleam. And the light made a path of gold from the door to Rob's pillow.

"Rob, are you awake?" she whispered.

"Yes, I can't go to sleep."

"I know," Mama said. She placed the lamp carefully on a table and sat down on the edge of the bed. Her lovely face was sad, but tonight her eyes had a new and steady look.

"I've decided something," she said. "We can't stay here always with your grandparents. They had to take us in, and I am grateful. But this is their home, not ours. Somehow I am going to find a way to earn some money. Then we can move to another place."

"Back to San Francisco?" Rob asked eagerly.

"No. That is too far away, and we don't belong there any more. We belong in New England, where the Frosts have lived for 250 years. I'll see whether I can teach in a school somewhere. Then we can move near the school,

112

maybe live by ourselves so things will be more like they used to be. Jeanie can sing again and not be afraid of making noise. And you, Rob, can whistle whenever you feel like it."

"When can we go?" Rob asked.

"I hope as soon as school starts in the fall," Mama said. "Meantime, you don't have to stay moping indoors like this. Why don't you take long walks the way you used to?"

"It's no fun walking in this smoky town. I've already been down by the mills and the dam and the water."

"But you could follow the river and go outside the town into the country," Mama suggested. "Why don't you go exploring? Maybe you would learn to like New England after all."

"Maybe," Rob said. "I'll try."

Mama gave Rob a quick hug. Then she drew back the heavy dark curtains and opened the window. "How sweet Grandma's lilac blossoms

smell tonight. And you should see how bright
the stars are shining!"

Rob jumped out of bed to see. With Mama
he leaned out the window. "The stars shine like
gold in the sky," he thought, "in the New England sky."

While he looked, Mama softly said part of her
favorite poem by Robert Herrick:

"Her eyes the glow-worm lend thee
The shooting stars attend thee
    And the elves also
    Whose little eyes glow
Like the sparks of fire, befriend thee.

Let not the dark thee cumber;
What though the moon does slumber?
    The stars of the night
    Will lend thee their light,
Like tapers clear, without number."

After Rob went back to bed, Mama left, taking the lamp with her, but the room did not turn

dark and gray. Rob could still see outside, just above the elm tree, a cluster of stars. He went to sleep thinking, "Tomorrow I'll go for a long walk. But this time I'll not be a giant, stepping over everything. Instead I'll be an explorer. Who knows what I might discover!"

The next day and all that summer, Rob went exploring. At Mama's suggestion, he kept a copybook to improve his writing and spelling. Each day when he came home after his walk, he wrote down for her the things he had discovered. Now at the end of summer, his copybook was almost full of words.

One night Rob showed his notebook to Jeanie. "Every word here means something special," he said. "I like the 'B' page best. See all the things I have found that begin with 'B': 'Birches,' 'Birds,' 'Butterflies,' 'Brooks,' and 'Blueberries.' Those blueberries were good." He paused to smack his lips.

115

"The 'W' page is really just as special, though," he went on, showing Jeanie. " 'Walls' that I climbed over, 'Water wells' that I looked into, 'Woods' that I walked through, and 'Woodchucks' that I watched."

Jeanie turned the pages back. "I like your 'F' page," she said. "This is where you have written 'Fireflies.' Remember we saw fireflies for the first time when Mama let us stay up? Grandma gave us a jam jar one evening to catch some of them in."

"Yes, but look here. The 'H' page wasn't any fun," Rob said. " 'Hornet!' Remember when I got stung by a white-tailed hornet?"

Mama came into Rob's room. She was smiling and her eyes were shining. "You can write a good new word on the 'H' page," she said, " 'Home.' Tomorrow we're going to find a new home in Salem. That's a village not far from here, just across the state line in New Hampshire. I have just learned that I can teach in the district school there."

Jeanie clapped her hands.

"Hurray!" cried Rob, writing "HOME" in big letters. "You'll still be our teacher, won't you, Mama? But this time in a real-honest-to-goodness schoolhouse.

"School," Rob said, turning pages. "That's a new word for the 'S' page." He wrote the word and closed his notebook.

Mama and Rob and Jeanie all hugged one another joyfully. "But now," Mama said, "I've thought of one more word for the 'S' page: 'Sleep.' That's what we all need, for tomorrow we go exploring in Salem."

"How do you spell 'Salem'?" Rob asked. "I'll write it down, too. There just isn't any end to special words, words that *do* things."

Swinging Birches

Rob was the first into the schoolyard. "Hey, there, Rob!" Charlie Peabody called to him.

"Wait for me," Charlie's sister called.

The thirty-five pupils in Mrs. Frost's district school were pouring out the door for recess. For a half hour everybody could do what he liked. Rob never had so many boys and girls to play with.

Charlie was the most fun of all. He wasn't afraid of anything. His sister, Sabra, was fun, too. Everybody called her "Sabe." She could throw a baseball like a boy, and she could run almost as fast as Rob and Charlie. Now she ran after the two boys over to the clump of birch trees growing at the edge of the yard.

"Have you ever climbed a birch tree?" Charlie asked Rob.

"No, we didn't have skinny white birches like these in California. We had redwoods," Rob said. "Nobody could climb such giant trees. What's special about climbing birches?"

"You can ride them," Charlie said. "I'll climb up to show you."

"Let me show him," Sabra said, excitedly. Her long dark curls bounced on her neck.

Charlie ignored Sabra and jumped into the crotch of the tree where three slender trunks spread out and up. Then he started climbing the tallest trunk. At first he went up fast, but as he went higher, he went slower. Carefully he inched his way almost to the top.

"Look out," he called below. "Here I come!" Holding on to the branch with his hands, he flung his feet out. Down he came kicking through the air, bending the branch with him.

When he was almost to the ground, he nimbly jumped off. The branch swung back up in place, black and white against the blue September sky. "Gee," Rob said. "You looked like an acrobat, coming down on a swinging trapeze."

"He felt like one, too," Sabra said. "You'll see. Shall I go next?"

"No, let Rob try it if he thinks he knows how," Charlie said.

"I think I do," said Rob.

He promptly stepped into the crotch where the three white trunks branched off. "Maybe you'd better take the shortest one," Sabra said.

Rob looked up along the chalky white trunks with their black markings into the canopy of yellow-gold leaves above him. "No, I'll try the biggest trunk, same as Charlie."

"All right," said Charlie, "but remember to

go slow and easy toward the top. It's tricky getting clear up to the right spot for kicking off. You have to sneak up to the top, sort of light, something like a squirrel."

Sabra agreed. "If you kick off too soon, you can't bend the tree clear down to the ground. You'll just be stuck, hanging up there like a bat in the daytime." She giggled at the thought that Rob could ever look like a bat.

Rob hesitated. "How will I know when I get to the right spot for kicking off?"

Charlie answered. "After you've done it a few times, you'll just know, that's all. You can tell mostly by the way it feels when you get there. Don't worry if you don't do it right the first time. Hardly anybody does."

"Well, I'll try." Rob put his arm around the tree trunk as high as he could reach. Then he wrapped his legs around below. Pulling himself up, he climbed fairly fast at first.

Halfway up the tree sturdy limbs branched out from the trunk. For a short way Rob used them like steps on a ladder. Higher up there were only small slim branches, almost like twigs. He didn't dare step on these slim branches.

Now there was just the slender main trunk of the tree left for Rob to climb. It tapered to a point not far above him, swaying in the breeze. "Like a feather duster," he thought, "with a bunch of yellow-brown leaves on top."

How much farther could he go? Rob looked down at Charlie and Sabra. Jeanie was there, too, now. They were watching his every move.

"Shall I try now?" Rob called down. "Have I reached the right spot?"

"I can't tell from down here," Charlie answered. "How does it feel?"

Rob took a deep breath. "As if I'll spill over, tree and all, if I go much farther."

"You're almost there then. Be careful."

Carefully Rob moved up an inch. The branch swayed from his weight. Carefully he crawled another inch. Was the branch beginning to bend? He held on tight and shifted his weight just the least bit to keep his balance.

"Like an acrobat," Rob thought.

One more inch! Suddenly he could feel the tree starting to dip under him. "Look out!" he called below. "Here I come!"

Like Charlie, Rob flung himself off feet first, holding with both hands to the bending branch. Down through the air he sailed. Swish!

At first he gasped. Then he laughed out loud as he let go and tumbled on the ground. "Whee!" he said, picking himself up. "That was dandy —the most fun I have ever had."

Charlie clapped him on the back. "You did it just right, and that was your first time."

Sabra beamed. This new boy, Rob, was going to be fun. Jeanie beamed, too, proud of him.

"Don't you want to try swinging from the tree, Jeanie?" Sabra asked.

Jeanie backed away, looking scared. "Oh, no. Girls can't swing birches."

"Oh, can't they!" Sabra said. "Watch me!"

124

Swift and sure as a squirrel, she started racing up along the branches.

Rob threw back his head and watched with delight. He had never known a girl like that. Jeanie caught her breath. She herself could never do that, never in all the world. To Charlie it was an old story. He knew his sister was as much at home in a tree as on the ground.

Suddenly the schoolbell rang. There was Mrs. Frost in the doorway with the big brass bell in her hand. Recess was over.

Jeanie and Charlie ran promptly toward the schoolhouse. Rob waited to see how Sabe would come dipping down from the birch tree. Could she swing down as well as Charlie had?

In another moment down she came, her blue dress fluttering. "She's like a blue butterfly," Rob thought, but he was too shy to tell her.

"Gee," he said, as she lit on the ground. "You did it best of all, Sabe."

Sabra laughed with pleasure. "You'll soon be best, Rob, if you keep on swinging birches. You are the best beginner I ever saw." She reached in her pocket. "Look, here's a leaf I picked for you from the tip-top of the tree."

Rob took the long pointed golden leaf. "Thanks. I'll put it in my speller. Come on, we're late. Let's race across the yard."

Together they reached the worn stone step by the schoolhouse door. "It's a tie!" Rob said.

"Sh! Your mother is starting to read," Sabra said, smoothing down her dark bangs over her forehead. She tip-toed into the room.

Rob, his scuffed shoes squeaking, went to his seat. Mrs. Frost looked up from her book but said nothing to the two latecomers. When she started reading aloud again, Rob opened his desk lid. He put his yellow leaf between two pages of his spelling book. "This way it will keep nice and smooth," he thought.

For a while he did not listen to his mother's voice. She always read aloud after recess. "So you can all quiet down," she said, "after running and whooping around like wild Indians."

At first Rob and Jeanie were shy about Mama's being teacher. They were afraid everyone would call them "teacher's pets." But soon they knew everything was going to be all right.

"She's different from the other teachers we've had," the children said.

"How?" Rob asked. "How is she different?"

"Because she isn't cross like most teachers have been," said a big boy.

"Because she helps me with my arithmetic," Sabra said. "I used to hate arithmetic. The other teachers went too fast for me."

"Because she helps me with geography," Charlie said. "I never knew all the states before. She has been in many states, like Ohio and California. In other countries, too, like Scotland."

"Because she reads stories and poems to us every day," others chimed in. "The other teachers never did."

Everyone in the room, from the biggest to the smallest, thought Mrs. Frost's reading was the best part of the day. Rob thought so, too, but today he didn't listen. He had his own adventures to think about. He could hardly wait to swing from another birch.

The next day on the way home from school, he found a birch that was different. To his surprise, as he climbed, he found bunches of purple wild grapes. They hung from a vine that hugged the tree trunk and looped out on some of the high branches.

Rob forgot about swinging from the tree and began to eat grapes. He popped one purple grape after another into his mouth. How juicy, how delicious they seemed. They were so slippery good that he swallowed them skin and all!

"Throw me some, Rob. They're too high for me to reach," called Jeanie down below.

"All right," Rob called down to his sister. "Get ready to catch them." He threw down one purple bunch, then another.

Jeanie missed catching the grapes. She started to look for them in the ferns and grass.

"They're scattered all about on the ground," she complained. "Get me a good bunch."

"All right," Rob said. "I'll bend down a lower branch for you. Grab it. Then you can pick your own grapes off it."

Swish! Down through the air came Rob, bringing the branch loaded with grapes. "Here, hold on," he said. He jumped off and handed her the tip of branch. "Grab it," he said.

Eagerly Jeanie reached for the branch and caught hold of it with both hands. Then up went the branch, up went the grapes, and up went Jeanie, kicking and screaming.

"Let go," Rob called. "Let go!"

Jeanie merely held on for dear life. She was afraid to let go and drop to the ground. She was afraid to stay up in the tree. She was afraid to do anything. There she hung like a little scared monkey.

Rob laughed to make her laugh. He made a joke about the tree picking her instead of her picking the grapes.

But Jeanie wouldn't laugh. She couldn't. She just clung to the branch with her legs dangling about. She let her head fall back. Her hat with its shiny ribbon floated to the ground. Her long red-gold hair streamed down her back. She shut her eyes in the sun's brightness. Still she hung on. One shoe fell off, then another.

Rob tried again. "Look! You can drop to the ground. It isn't far."

Jeanie didn't answer. She was too busy holding on. Her wrists stretched tight.

Rob did not know what to do. "Let go," he said. "You're light. I can catch you."

Still Jeanie just hung there. "Almost like a bunch of grapes herself," Rob thought.

"All right. I know how to get you down," he called. In another minute he was up in the tree, crawling out on Jeanie's branch. In no time they were swinging down together.

They landed safely on the ground. Jeanie took a deep breath. She uncurled her stiff fingers. Then she giggled. "I still haven't had any grapes," she said.

Quickly Rob got her a perfect bunch. "Here, eat these. If you eat more, you will weigh more. Then you can pull the branch down yourself. That would be better than letting the branch pull you up again."

"Anything would be better than that," Jeanie said. "After this I think I'll let my big brother pick my grapes for me."

"A Boy's Will Is the Wind's Will"

MR. WOODBURY, who lived in a neat white frame house, was the Frosts' landlord. He told them he was afraid their first winter in New England would be long and bitterly cold. "It's going to be a real gripper," he said. "I feel it in my bones."

The Frosts rented two upstairs rooms from Mr. Woodbury, but they had the use of the whole house. "I'm proud to have the new teacher living here," Mrs. Woodbury said. "I like to hear children's voices and a boy whistling in the house again. And it's good to cook for someone who enjoys my cooking as much as this boy."

Rob smacked his lips. " 'Specially when you have apple pie for breakfast," he said.

Every morning and evening Rob brought in wood to stuff into the big black cooking range. "That stove is as hungry as I am," he said. "I have to keep carrying and carrying."

Sometimes Jeanie helped with the supper dishes at the big iron sink. She didn't mind working in the kitchen because it was always warm there.

In the evenings, Jeanie liked to study her lessons at the round dining room table. It seemed cozy and warm in front of the Franklin stove. Rob studied his spelling at the table. In the same circle of yellow lamplight, Mama graded school papers. There was no heat in the parlor and no heat in the upstairs bedrooms where the Frosts slept.

One bitterly cold night Jeanie shivered as she undressed in the room she shared with Mama.

Mama said, "You're just like the wee bird in that old Scottish verse:

> 'A wee bird sat upon a tree
> When the year was dune and auld
> And aye it cheepit sae peetiously
> My but it's cauld, cauld.' "

Jeanie just whimpered and said, "This isn't the kind of home I thought we were going to have. It isn't our house any more than Grandpa's was. I'm sure his house is warmer."

Mama sighed. Then she said cheerfully, "In a way this is more our home than Grandpa's was. Every time you dry dishes and Rob carries wood, you are doing your share. And I pay the Woodburys regularly for our room and board. So we aren't indebted to them in the way we were to Grandpa. Now I'm sure that Grandpa is proud of us because we can look out for ourselves. In his last letter he said he admired people who earned their own way."

134

Mama hugged Jeanie. "Now, lass, hop into bed. Instead of kneeling on the cold floor tonight, you may say your prayers under the covers, if you wish. The warm freestone Rob put there will toast your feet."

Jeanie hurried to get into bed and tripped over her long woolen nightgown. Then she jumped up and slid under the covers with a shriek. "It's freezing! The sheets are like ice! Rob forgot to put in the stone."

"Here you are, Jeanie," called Rob from the doorway. He was lugging a big flat stone wrapped in thick newspaper. He gave the stone to Jeanie who pushed it quickly down between the cotton flannel sheets.

"Now I don't know where to put it first," she said. "I'm too cold to know."

"I'm sorry that I didn't bring it sooner," he said, "but I started to read the paper, the *New Hampshire Gazette.*"

Mama was glad to have Rob show greater interest in reading. "What did you read in the paper?" she asked.

"Well, I saw a piece about a man named Whittier, who's a real live poet. And, Mama," Rob went on eagerly, "this poet lives in New England and comes to New Hampshire often. I was surprised. I thought all poets lived long ago in old England or Scotland—like Robert Herrick and Robert Burns."

Mama laughed. "No. There have been fine poets in New England, too. Have you ever looked at the books of poetry in the front parlor? We'll read them sometime.

"Two poets, Mr. Emerson and Mr. Longfellow, lived near Boston. They died just a couple of years ago. Mr. Whittier is still writing bonny poems. He writes about farms and animals and snowy New Hampshire winters."

Jeanie spoke up. "I hate winter."

136

"That's because you stick in the house all the time," Rob said. "If you'd stay out and play with Charlie and Sabe and me after school, you'd have fun."

"No, thanks," said Jeanie. "It's hard enough for Mama and me to walk all that way home from school in the cold."

"That walk in the fresh air gives you your pretty pink cheeks," Mama said.

Her mother's praise made Jeanie's cheeks even pinker. Mama pulled her shawl close around her shoulders, and said, "Now I must go downstairs and correct more school papers."

Jeanie pushed the stone down under her feet and curled her toes around it. "Now the bed is getting warmer. Good night."

Rob started for his own room. He called back, "Just wait till we have a thumping big snowstorm. Then you'll like winter."

Jeanie didn't answer. She just snuggled

137

deeper under the covers until only a patch of her reddish hair was sticking out.

Rob laughed. "You're just like a woodchuck going down in his hole. Too bad you can't sleep all winter the way he does."

The very next day it looked as if there might be a snowstorm. In school Rob looked out the window. The sky grew darker. The pale sun disappeared. A few large snowflakes zigzagged down out of the low gray sky.

It was Friday morning, but Rob dreaded the coming afternoon. He liked the idea that the next day would be Saturday, but first he had to get through the afternoon. That afternoon Mama would call on some of her pupils to read their compositions out loud. Rob didn't mind writing compositions. What scared him was standing up and reading them. Mama said, "Remember the pupils are just your friends." But that didn't seem to lessen his stage fright.

Rob looked over at Sabra who was finishing her composition. Nothing ever bothered Sabe. That was one reason Rob liked her so much. She looked as cheerful as a chickadee.

Suddenly he remembered that Sabe had passed a note over to him yesterday. Until now he had been too busy to answer. He tried to remember the polite way Grandpa and Mama started their letters to each other. He would begin his note in the same way.

Quickly he bent over a piece of lined paper torn from his tablet. "Dear Sabe," he wrote. "I read your letter with great pleasure and will try and answer it in a very few lines . . . I have got to read a composition after recess and I hate to offaly.

"I have got to stop now so as to learn my Geography. From your loving   Rob."

Quickly Rob poked Charlie who sat next to him. Charlie grinned and passed the note on to his sister. Rob pretended to read his geography, but over the top of his book he watched Sabe read the note. Would she feel sorry for him, being scared to read a composition?

Sabra smiled at Rob. Then she silently made the words with her lips: "Don't worry."

Her smile made Rob feel better. He expected her to crumple his note for the wastebasket, but she folded it neatly. She took all the pencils from her wooden pencil box and pulled out a small drawer at the bottom. This was her secret drawer! There she hid Rob's note.

Rob's mother rapped on her desk with a ruler. "It's time for geography class. The pupils in the geography class may come up front to recite their lesson."

In a hurry Sabra pushed in the secret drawer and placed the pencils on top. Then she slid the lid back over everything.

Rob was delighted. He thought, "She likes

my note well enough to keep it." He smiled at her as he went up front for geography.

From time to time Rob looked out the window. Now the snow was really falling. It was covering the schoolyard like a soft white blanket.

Everybody ate lunch, sitting around the school stove. Afterward Charlie called, "Let's go outside. The snow's just right for playing a game of fox and geese."

Mama looked out anxiously. Jeanie hung back, but Rob and Sabe and several others ran to the wooden pegs for coats and caps and mittens. Then they went whooping out the door to play fox and geese. During the running and shrieking in the snow, Rob completely forgot about having to read a composition.

But when Mama rang the big brass bell, Rob remembered. As everybody pushed back inside the school, his heart sank. Now there was no escape. He would have to read out loud.

142

Then all the children had a surprise. Mrs. Frost said, "Quiet, boys and girls. Since it is snowing harder and harder, we may be in for a real storm. I have decided to skip the composition readings today. Everybody had better start for home at once. School is dismissed."

"Hooray!" Rob cried.

In two minutes everyone was outside, making new tracks toward home. Mama and Jeanie bent their heads low against the pelting snow. They followed close behind Rob, stepping in his footprints. The deeper the snow got, the more Rob enjoyed it, but Mama and Jeanie were worn out by the time they reached home.

As they pulled off their heavy wet things, Jeanie whispered, "I hate snow. It's so cold and so deep, and so wet."

The landlady said cheerfully, "Sakes, child, it's only weather. You'll be all right. Now drink this warm milk I fixed for you."

Mama said, "I'm only sorry we had to miss the Friday afternoon readings." Rob said nothing. He just grinned and drank his milk.

That night the Frosts gathered close to the Franklin stove in the dining room. Mama read aloud Emerson's "The Snow Storm" and Whittier's long poem, "Snowbound."

Outside the wind whistled. Snow and sleet ticked against the windows of the house. Snow drifted high against the sills, gleaming white in the lamplight.

Inside, warm and cozy, the children listened to Mama's clear voice. Finally, just before bedtime, Mama read one last poem, this time a poem by Mr. Longfellow. Every verse ended with lines that sang themselves over and over in Rob's head, even after he was snug in bed:

"A boy's will is the wind's will
    And the thoughts of youth are long long
        thoughts."

A New Pair
of Shoes

ALL THAT WINTER Rob delighted in tramping through the white countryside. New England took on new beauty as part of a fresh white world. Each new snowfall trimmed the pines and fir trees with popcorn strings and balls of snow. The white carpet on the dark floor of the woods grew thicker and thicker.

Every Saturday after doing odd jobs at home, Rob and Charlie went exploring. Their shoes made a chain of fresh footprints as they tramped across the fields and through the woods.

With Charlie's help, Rob learned to read animals' footprints in the snow. It became as easy for him as reading news articles in the *New Hampshire Gazette*. The tiny tracks of a meadow mouse told him where one had skittered past. The larger track of a cottontail rabbit showed where one had hopped about. The flat-footed, pigeon-toed tracks of the porcupine showed where one had waddled.

"I'd like to see a bear or a deer someday," Rob said. "Close up."

Charlie answered. "The bears are asleep, hiding in caves most of the winter," he explained. "And deer are so shy and scared that it's hard to get close to them."

Rob thought Saturdays with Charlie were great fun. When the boys weren't tracking animals, they chattered and whistled like birds. They romped in the snow like rabbits and chased each other like squirrels.

Outdoor life was hard on Rob's shoes. When Mama discovered big holes in them, she said, "I can't pay much to have them fixed. Find out what the cobbler can do with them."

"But it's Saturday," objected Rob. "I don't want to spend all afternoon in the shoe shop."

Mama insisted. "You can't play out in the snow again until your shoes are fixed. You'll catch a cold, or worse."

When Rob walked into the shoe shop, Mr. Smith, the cobbler, looked up from his bench and smiled. "You're the schoolteacher's boy, aren't you? What can I do for you, young man?"

Rob liked the cobbler. He was almost twelve, but he had never been called a young man before. He took off his wet shoes and handed them over. "Can you mend these old shoes?" he asked. "My mama hopes it won't cost too much. And I hope it won't take too long." Rob stood in his stocking feet and watched anxiously.

"Yes, I can fix them, but they're pretty much worn out. Do they fit you all right?"

147

"They're a little tight," Rob confessed. "They pinch. I guess my feet are growing like the rest of me."

Mr. Smith said, "Perhaps instead of mending these, I should make you new ones."

"Oh, I'm sure Mama can't pay for new shoes. I never told her these hurt me."

The shoemaker looked sharply at Rob. Even in his stocking feet, Rob stood tall. His rumpled fair hair fell down over his forehead. His blue eyes were anxious.

Mr. Smith liked Rob's looks. "My helper went to Lynn last week to work in a shoe factory," he said. "How would you like to learn how to make and mend shoes? You could work for me on Saturdays and earn a little money. And you could earn a pair of shoes for yourself."

Rob asked, "You mean my mother wouldn't have to pay anything for them?"

"Not if you pay me in work on Saturdays. We

can begin right now on your new shoes, and you can wear them home tonight."

How surprised and pleased Mama would be! Rob suddenly made up his mind. "All right," he said. "I'd like to work for you, but I don't know anything about making new shoes. I just know how to make holes in old ones."

Mr. Smith laughed. "Today just watch me and learn by looking. We'll start at the beginning. First find the wooden last or pattern which is your size over there on the shelf. Then we'll use the last for building your shoes."

All that afternoon, Rob handed tools and materials as Mr. Smith asked for them. It was exciting to watch his very own pair of shoes take shape. Mr. Smith worked fast, explaining as he went along. He did everything from cutting and shaping the leather to stitching and nailing the parts together.

Rob's eyes opened wide when he saw Mr.

Smith clap a handful of nails in his mouth. "Don't you ever swallow one?" Rob asked.

"Never a one," said Mr. Smith. "You get used to having them, just like your teeth."

Rob clapped a handful of nails into his own mouth. But he quickly spit them out again like watermelon seeds.

The cobbler said, "Better not try that till you get used to the work."

Finally Mr. Smith nailed the heel on one of the shoes. "Let me try to nail the heel on the other shoe," Rob begged. With great care, he did exactly what the shoemaker had done.

"Fine!" Mr. Smith said. "Soon you will be good enough to join the brothers. Shakespeare referred to shoemakers when he said, 'We few, we happy few, we band of brothers.'"

With final trimming, sandpapering, and polishing, Mr. Smith finished the work on the shoes. "Here you are, young man," he said.

Eagerly Rob tried on the shoes. He took a few steps forward. Then he turned a handspring. "They fit just right," he said, "with enough space to grow in. Thank you, sir."

"The best way to thank me is to show up next Saturday for work!"

Mama was delighted with Rob's sturdy new shoes. "And to think you are going to pay for them yourself. I am proud of you. The money you earn will be a big help, too."

Jeanie said, "Make me a pair, won't you? I want a pair of slippers."

Rob grinned. "Maybe sometime. But I'd rather go into the woods this spring and find you a pink lady slipper growing there."

Even in April spring still seemed a long way off. Rob had little free time to spend in the woods. He was pleased to be earning money in the shoe shop, but he missed having fun outdoors with Charlie. Then one day he had a holiday, but it started off wrong.

Mama caught a bad cold. Thursday afternoon she announced there would be no school on Friday. Rob and Charlie made great plans for spending the whole day together. Next morning Charlie glumly reported that he and Sabe had to go to Boston with their mother. They would be gone all day. Rob's holiday was ruined.

He ran errands for his mother and did odd jobs for the landlady. After lunch there was nothing more for him to do in the house, and he didn't want to go exploring by himself. Outside it was cold, gray, and raw.

Glumly he put on his overcoat, which was becoming too small for him. He reached in his pocket for his mittens. Ugh! They were still soggy. He had forgotten to put them by the stove to dry. What a mess! And where was his cap with the earflaps? By the time he found it in a dark corner of the closet, he felt glummer than ever. Today nothing was right.

He jammed the cap on his head, jerked the flaps down over his ears, went outdoors and slammed the door behind him. What a dismal day! He turned up his coat collar and pushed his hands in his pockets. Then he struck out across the field, kicking snow with every step.

He kept going until he came to the place where the woods began. Should he go on around the woods or into the woods? Or should he give up his lonely walk and go back home? He tarried under the drooping branches of a hemlock tree, covered with soft powdery snow.

"Caw," came the sudden harsh cry of a crow on a branch high above him.

Rob looked up, startled. The bird looked glossy black against the white snow. "Caw, yourself," he answered.

"Caw, Caw," the crow replied.

Rob was sure the bird was playing a game with him. "Are you making fun of me? All right, then. How's this? Caw, Caw, Caw!"

The crow cocked his shiny eye at Rob and

154

ruffled his wings. Then he hopped along the bough, knocking off some of the powdery snow right into Rob's upturned face. Rob was so surprised that he burst out laughing.

"Why, you rascal!" he said. "I'll get you." He scooped up some snow and threw it at the crow, but the snow scattered in the air. It didn't even touch the bird's tail feathers.

"Caw, Caw," the crow mocked. And off he flew into the woods.

Rob laughed again. Then eagerly he plunged into the woods. He forgot about being lonely. The crow had disappeared, but he heard a loud knocking in a tall pine tree. Looking up, he saw a woodpecker drumming away at the rough trunk. The bird sounded as though he were beating a drum in a loud, fierce rat-a-tat.

"Like an Indian, a hostile Indian," Rob said to himself. "He's wearing his bright red war bonnet. I'll be an Indian, too. I must go warn my own tribe in the hidden valley. The enemy is on the warpath."

Swift and silent as an Indian scout, Rob made his way in and out among the trees. Finally he reached the other side of the woods. He crept along behind the stone wall by an orchard. Suddenly he saw something that made him forget his game. He stopped and caught his breath.

There just over the low wall was a deer, nibbling at the bark of an apple tree. Rob was so close he could have reached out and touched her. Instead, he stood as still as a stone.

The doe turned her head and saw Rob. Quietly, calmly, she looked back at him with her big soft eyes. For a long moment the boy and the deer gazed at each other. Then, the deer moved slowly on until out of sight.

Rob's heart beat fast. He was surprised because the deer wasn't frightened at seeing him. Perhaps since he was quiet and alone, she felt that he was not a stranger. "That's it," Rob thought joyfully. "She thinks I belong here, outdoors, just like her, and I do. I belong here even when I'm by myself."

By now the short winter day was almost over. One star had pricked its way through the cloudy sky. All the way home Rob was full of wonder at the marvels of the afternoon, an afternoon that had started off so full of gloom and had ended so full of gladness. He could hardly wait to tell his family about everything.

At home Rob cheerfully changed his wet clothes. Mama was feeling better. She sat reading in the rocker by the stove. She asked, "What did you do outdoors all by yourself?"

"I wasn't all by myself," Rob teased. His blue eyes were shining.

"Who was with you?" Jeanie asked.

Then Rob told his mother and Jeanie about the funny crow and the woodpecker. He told them about pretending to be an Indian. And he tried to tell them about the doe with big soft eyes that didn't run from him.

"Is that all?" Jeanie asked.

"All!" Rob was dismayed. He realized that he hadn't used the right words to describe his wonderful afternoon. He hadn't expressed the magic of it all—the birds, the snowy woods, the tawny deer, and the feeling that he belonged outdoors. How could he speak more clearly?

"There must be a way to make people understand" he thought. "Some day," he promised himself, "I'll learn how to say things the way I feel them. I'll find the right words."

"Promises to Keep"

DURING THE NEXT few years, Rob always had a job. The first summer he worked in the shoe shop in Salem. Other summers, glad to be out-doors, he worked on a nearby farm. Then he, Mama, and Jeanie could live in a wing of the farmhouse free.

Rob liked working under the hot sun. He learned to do all sorts of things: how to swing an ax, how to mow with a scythe, how to load hay on a wagon with a pitchfork, how to build a stack of hay. The one job he hated was crank-ing the grindstone while the farmer sharpened tools. Turning the crank made his arms ache

159

till he thought they would drop off, yet he had to keep on turning.

Sometimes he could take time for a walk or a swim. Often on clear nights he lay in the grass, gazing at the star-spangled sky. Dreamily he watched while the stars moved slowly and steadily across the dome of the sky that curved high over his head.

During the summer Rob's face became tanned from the sun. His eyes blazed blue from under locks of straw colored hair. He grew taller and stronger by the day, and he always was willing to tackle any man-sized job, especially at harvest time.

Neighbor farmers all got together to help one another in their fields. Rob liked listening to the farmers talk, the way they said things, the twang of their voices.

The first summer Rob worked on the farm, Mama said, "You're beginning to sound like a

160

farmer yourself, lad. Maybe when you grow up, you will own a farm of your own, but don't forget books are important, too. This fall you must go to a good high school. We'll find a way somehow for you to go."

Finally Grandpa Frost came to the rescue and offered to arrange for Rob to attend high school in Lawrence. He paid Rob's fare back and forth between Salem and Lawrence. Any time after school that Rob wanted to, he could stay all night at his grandparents' house, which was only a short distance away.

Now at fourteen, Rob found himself in the thick of things at Lawrence High School. He studied hard, especially Latin. He played hard, especially baseball. He wrote articles for the school paper. He made many friends.

Rob spent four years in Lawrence High School. During these four years, three things happened that he considered very important:

He wrote his first poem.
He met the girl he wanted to marry.
He made high honors in his class.

The poem came to Rob suddenly. One day he read a chapter in Prescott's book *Conquest of Mexico.* The story filled him with pity for the ancient Indians of Mexico and their leader, Montezuma. He was proud of their fight against the Spanish invader Cortes, who tried to escape one night with his army. The Spanish called it "La Noche Triste"—the sorrowful night.

As Rob walked to his grandparents' house after class, he kept thinking of that chapter in the book. Prescott's words carried him far from the windy, cold March day in Lawrence. He saw instead the warm, dark city of Mexico. He could hear the muffled tramp of Spanish soldiers and the clop of horses, as the Spanish tried to steal away from the sleeping city.

Soon the Indian sentinels were aroused and

began to sound the alarm. They blew on their conch shells. They beat on their huge snakeskin drum.

Rob became more and more excited as he recalled Prescott's stirring words about the Indians' attack: "A gathering sound was heard, like that of a mighty forest agitated by winds. It grew louder and louder . . . Then came a few stones and arrows . . . They fell every moment faster and more furious, till they thickened into a terrible tempest."

Rob himself felt the gathering wind, the darkness. His thoughts were in a tumult. Gradually he began to see and to hear the story in new words, his own words.

When he reached his grandparents' house, it was quiet. He stood in the kitchen and listened. The only sound he heard was the loud slow tick of the clock on the wall and the slow drip of water in the sink.

As though under a spell, he sat down at the kitchen table. Then quickly he started to write the story in verses. He began:

"Anon the cry comes down the line,
The portals wide are swung,
A long dark line moves out the gate,
And now the flight's begun."

As Rob wrote he felt a thrill of achievement. He felt just as he did when he first rode a birch down through the air with a swish. The verses fairly tumbled from his pencil onto paper. Soon he had the poem completed.

The next day he gave the poem to the editor of the high school paper, an older boy at school. Anxiously he watched the older boy read the poem. Would he like it? Would he think it was worth printing in the paper?

The boy read the poem very carefully. Then finally he looked up at Rob. "I didn't know you wrote poetry," he said.

Rob tried to answer cautiously. "I didn't know it either until now," he said.

The boy was curious. "What made you write a poem?" he asked.

"I don't know," Rob said shyly. Then he grinned. "Who knows what makes a frog jump?"

Rob's poem, "La Noche Triste," was printed in the school paper. From then on, the brightest and prettiest girl in his class looked at him with new interest. Then he blushed with pleasure at her noticing him.

The girl's name was Elinor White. Rob began to walk home with her after school, carrying her books. He discovered that he greatly enjoyed talking with her. When she laughed, her laugh sounded like a bird's song, but she didn't giggle in the way some silly girls did.

Elinor wasn't a lively tomboy, good at climbing trees, but Rob thought she was as graceful as a birch. She wasn't a bookworm, but he noticed that books were like friends to her. Now whenever he wrote a new poem, he hoped most of all that she would like it.

By the time Rob and Elinor were seniors, they were close friends. To their surprise they found that they were rivals, too. One day the school principal said to Rob, "You need to watch out. Elinor White is making good grades and catching up with you. She may be head of the class instead of you!"

Rob smiled and said, "Good! I hope she is. She deserves it."

In the end, the two were tied for first place. Each made a speech at graduation. In addition, Rob wrote the class hymn, a poem. He kept stealing glances at the program where the following credit line appeared: "Words by Robert L. Frost. Music by Beethoven."

On this day Rob was completely happy. By now he had written several poems. He had found an interesting girl. He had won honors. Grandpa had offered to get him a summer job in the mill. And Grandpa had arranged to send him to Dartmouth College next fall.

The future looked rosy, but things didn't turn out right for Rob. Nobody seemed to care whether he wrote poetry or not. The mill job kept him cooped up indoors. He missed Elinor, who went to a faraway college in New York State. At his own college, he was homesick.

He grew tired of being shut up with dusty books in dusty classrooms. He grew tired of roughhousing with the other boys. Frequently, he felt he had to escape by taking long walks in the woods all by himself. When he returned from these walks, his fraternity brothers asked, "What do you do in the woods all alone?"

Rob couldn't explain, so he tried to make a joke out of his trips. "I gnaw bark," he said. How could he explain that he was homesick with a big lump in his throat? Wanting to be alone, he turned to poetry to express his bubbled-up thoughts and feelings.

On one cold walk he remembered with longing a dazzling day during the summer just before he left home. He had watched a bright butterfly, whirling with others in the bright sunshine. Now, of course, the butterfly was gone, and the grass was gray. Still he yearned to describe the butterfly in a poem.

Letters from Rob's mother were discouraging. She wasn't well and was having trouble with some of the big boys in her new school. She didn't know how to handle them.

Suddenly Rob quit college. He decided he was wasting his time there. He went home to help his mother.

Grandpa Frost was disturbed. He had hoped Rob would go through college and become a lawyer or a businessman. He had no patience with Rob, who now planned to help his mother and to write poetry when he could.

Rob's mother also was sorry he left college, but she was pleased when he spent his first day helping her in school. "He makes the big boys behave," she said to Jeanie. "Besides, he's a natural-born teacher."

And Elinor? What did she think? At this time she was much too happy and busy at her own college to think much about Rob.

For two years Rob was unsettled, wondering what to do. He taught school, worked in a mill, and helped out on a farm. Only to himself he admitted the truth, "The only thing I really want to be is a poet. And I can't earn a living by writing poems."

By now Rob was almost twenty years old. Lacking encouragement from others, he tried to keep writing poetry a secret. Night after night he wrote by the dim lamplight, simply for the

170

pleasure of writing. His only encouragement came from Mama.

Sometimes Rob mailed a poem to a magazine or paper, hoping it might be accepted, but it always came back. Nobody seemed to like it well enough to print it. One day when he came home from work, Mama called, "There's a letter for you. It's from a magazine in New York called *The Independent*."

Rob tore open the letter and said, "Probably it's just that new poem I sent there, coming back like all the rest."

Then he gave a shout! To his delight and amazement the editors of *The Independent* wrote they liked his poem called "My Butterfly." They would print it, and they would pay him for it. Did he have any other poems to send them?

"Do I!" Rob was blissfully happy. Now perhaps things would be different. Mama had always believed in him. Now even Grandpa might think he was worth something. More important, Elinor might again take an interest in him. Most important of all, he felt confident he was on the way to doing what he wanted to do, being what he wanted to be.

He remembered that once long ago he had promised himself he would find the right words, the right way to say what he really felt. That was a promise he was beginning to keep. He could do it by writing poetry.

Poet-Farmer

FOR A NUMBER of years, Robert Frost had a hard time selling his poems. Elinor White decided that did not matter. She thought that writing poetry was more important than selling it. To Rob's great joy they were married after she finished college. Both taught for awhile in his mother's private school.

They decided that Rob should get a college degree. Then someday he could teach in a college and write poetry, too. Again Grandpa Frost paid Rob's way, this time to Harvard where Rob's father had gone. Again Rob won honors, this time in the classics.

Soon Rob became very ill. He had to quit college before two years were up. Discouraged, he said, "Now I'll never get a degree!"

How was he to get well! He was sure two things would help—working outdoors and writing poetry. If only he had a little money, enough to buy a small farm!

Finally he and Elinor got up enough courage to seek help from Grandpa Frost. They had found a small farm near Derry, New Hampshire, which they liked. "It will be a good place for Rob to work," Elinor said to Grandpa.

Grandpa Frost snorted. "And for him to waste his time writing poetry!" he said. "I know that's what you're up to."

Finally Grandpa gave in. "All right," he said. "I'll buy the farm, this one-man, one-horse farm. I'll lend it to you. Promise me that if you don't make a go of poetry in a year, you'll settle down and get a sensible job!"

One year? Suddenly Rob was full of spunk again. "Give me twenty years! I'll make a go of poetry in twenty years!" He was half joking, but it took him almost that long.

Frost considered his years on the Derry farm very important, but his country neighbors couldn't see that he was getting anywhere. "How could he," they said, "when he sits up half the night, writing poetry which won't sell? Then he sleeps half the morning! Doesn't he know that 'early to bed and early to rise is the way to be healthy, wealthy, and wise'?"

People admitted that Frost was good at taking care of apple trees. And good at raising chickens. And good at riding or working his horse. But he didn't always remember to milk the cow at the proper times.

The Frosts raised a nice family of four bright children, three girls and a boy. The children, like their parents, stayed much to themselves.

175

Every spring Frost helped his neighbor, Baptiste, mend the stone wall that ran between their
farms. Once Baptiste said, "Good fences make
good neighbors." And Frost asked, "Why? Why

do they?" Then he added, "Something there is that doesn't love a wall."

Baptiste shook his head. "Great talker, that Frost, but not a proper farmer."

The editors of most magazines seemed to think Robert Frost was not a proper poet, either. One editor wrote him, "Your verses sound too much like talking."

"But that's the way I want them to sound," Frost said.

Another editor wrote, "Your poetry is all about farms and farmers. You sound like a farmer yourself."

Frost grinned. "There's nothing I'd rather be taken for, unless its a baseball pitcher," he joked. "And I'm not good enough for that."

Once in a long while *The Independent* printed one of Frost's poems. Not many people, however, even noticed that it was published.

By now the farm was his. Grandpa Frost had

left it to him when he died. What the farm gave him was time—time for being out of doors, time for thinking, time for writing. It gave him little else. But the Frosts were content.

One day Frost was jolted out of his contentment. He had spent his sixth winter on the farm. The village grocer appeared at the door, demanding he pay his large bill at the store. The grocer demanded cash.

Frost now knew that he would have to get a job to earn money. His mother was no longer living, but he recalled something she once had said, "Rob is a natural-born teacher."

The minister in the village had a suggestion. "Come to the Men's League meeting tomorrow night and read one of your poems. If you make a good impression, you may be invited to teach at Pinkerton Academy on the hill. The school needs an English teacher."

The idea of reading one of his poems to

178

strangers scared Frost. "I'll be like Tommy Tucker, singing for my supper," he muttered. But he knew that if he didn't, there might not be many more suppers for his family!

That night he scarcely slept. The next day he grew more and more nervous at the thought of reading at the meeting. If only he could get his mind off it!

Half in fun, half in earnest, Frost put pebbles in his shoes when he started the long walk to the village. "They'll hurt my feet so much, I won't be able to think about the poetry reading," he said to his wife.

But his plan didn't work. Limping along the road to the village, he was twice as miserable as before. He emptied the stones out of his shoes before he went inside. Now his feet were comfortable, but his mind was in a panic. He was tempted to return home.

In desperation he begged the minister, "Don't

call on me to read my poem in front of these people. I just can't do it."

"Then give the poem to me," the minister said, "and let me read it for you."

Robert Frost sat slumped in his seat while the preacher read his poem, "The Tuft of Flowers." Like most of his poems, this poem described a simple country scene. It expressed feelingly his "sheer morning gladness" at finding a tuft of flowers which had been left by the mower.

The audience listened quietly. People were moved by the last lines,

> " 'Men work together,' I told him from the heart,
> 'Whether they work together or apart.' "

There was a moment's silence. Then everyone clapped. Smiling and nodding, they looked at this shy, awkward man with new interest and admiration. It would be good to have a poet like him teaching English at the Academy.

And so that spring, Robert Frost was launched on his teaching career. He was not shy in the classroom. He was warm and friendly. He stirred up the students to doing their best. All the students liked him. Many thought he was the best teacher they had ever had.

Wherever he went, Frost wanted to teach only part time. "There always has to be time for writing poetry," he said. "Even if teaching is quicker to pay the grocery bill."

In 1912 the Frosts sailed for England. By now they had sold Derry farm and wanted to live for a while in the land of the poet, Robert Herrick. They wanted to see where Robert Burns had lived and written. In England they rented a cottage in the country outside London. The Frost children ran about exploring, instead of going to school. They kept notebooks, writing about things they saw and did. Elinor, their mother, kept house in the little cottage.

Robert Frost kept busy, too. One chilly night he sat by the open fire, going through old poems he had brought from home. He burned some in the blaze, and he put others away to be worked on later. Then he sorted out all his favorite early poems that seemed to sing of the countryside at home.

"Why, there are enough poems here to make a book!" he said to Elinor as he looked at the collection. "I can start off with 'The Pasture' with its invitation, 'You come, too.' What shall I call the book?"

As he gazed into the fire, he remembered the lines from Longfellow which his mother had read to him many years before:

"A boy's will is the wind's will,
    And the thoughts of youth are long long
        thoughts."

"That's it!" he cried. "I'll call my book *A Boy's Will*. Now all I have to do is find someone in

London to publish the book. That won't be easy in a strange land."

But it was easy. An English firm brought the book out in April. It was a success in England, perhaps because the poems were so American. These were Frost's singing poems.

Next he gathered together his talking poems, beginning with "Mending Wall." He called this second book *North of Boston*. Word of the new book spread to America.

England was good to Robert Frost, but after World War I exploded in Europe, the Frosts left the meadows of old England to come back to the pastures of New England.

The Frost family landed in New York on Washington's birthday, 1915. Frost still was poor with very little money in his pocket. "No matter," he said to his wife. "We are coming home. The important thing is will I ever get a book published here at home?"

Walking down the street in New York City, he stopped at a newsstand. He spent almost his last fifty cents for a new magazine, *The New Republic*. There he discovered that his book *North of Boston* was being published in America that very month.

An exciting review of the book said about Frost, "He goes his own way regardless of anyone else's rules . . . and the result is a book of unusual power and sincerity."

Frost gave a long whistle. What a happy homecoming! Now he knew that his poems would be read in his own country. And he could continue to go his own way.

America's Poet

"GOING his own way" took Robert Frost through the authorship of many books of poetry, through family joys and sorrows, through prizes and public honors in many places. Before he died in 1963, his stride had taken him to all parts of our country. It had taken him to far away countries, including Israel, Greece, and Russia.

Wherever Frost went, his poetry opened doors for him. He even lost his fear of appearing on public platforms. This happened when he simply *said* his poems instead of trying to lecture and make speeches.

People everywhere were delighted to listen.

Often they asked him to say "Birches," a poem that had been swinging in his mind ever since he was a boy. Another favorite was "Stopping by Woods on a Snowy Evening." This one ended with the lines,

"But I have promises to keep,
And miles to go before I sleep,
And miles to go before I sleep."

Amherst and many other colleges claimed Robert Frost as teacher. Universities all over the country and abroad awarded him honorary degrees because of his poetry. With each degree came a bright colored hood of shining silk or satin or soft velvet.

"All together they will make a fine patchwork quilt," he said. "Bright as a rainbow and warm as a freestone on a cold winter night."

The climax came when Frost was invited to say a poem at the inauguration of John F. Kennedy in Washington, D. C., January 20, 1961.

On inauguration day, the air was bitterly cold, but the sun was dazzling on the snow and ice. It shone bright on tens of thousands of excited people who had gathered for the occasion. They lined the avenues and Capitol Plaza, bundled up in mufflers, furs, coats, and blankets.

All eyes were on the flag-bedecked platform where the nation's youngest President and the country's oldest poet were sitting. John F. Kennedy himself had invited Frost to attend and take part in the inauguration.

Neither President nor poet seemed to mind the freezing weather in Washington. Each of them had known deeper snows and colder days than this in New England.

"Besides," Frost thought as he waited on the platform, "today is a day to warm the cockles of the heart. Poets and statesmen are getting together at last."

Frost remembered how disappointed he had

been seventy-five years before, when he was a boy of eleven and couldn't come to the inauguration of President Cleveland. Now here he was eighty-six years old, the first poet ever asked to take part in an inauguration.

Frost rose with all others at the stirring sound of "The Star-Spangled Banner." As Marian Anderson sang this song, her rich voice rolled out on the clear cold air.

Cardinal Cushing of Boston gave a long and earnest prayer. The new Vice-President, Lyndon B. Johnson of Texas, took the oath of office. The new President would be sworn in later.

Soon it would be Frost's turn on the program. At Kennedy's request he would say his most patriotic poem, "The Gift Outright." This was an old poem, which he knew by heart. No need to be nervous over that!

But the poet was planning a surprise. Yesterday and until the last minute that very morning he had worked on a brand-new poem in honor of the President. He planned to read this poem because he hadn't really learned it yet. Nervously he felt in his pocket for the papers on which the poem was written to make sure they were there.

Suddenly Frost was introduced to the vast audience. He stood at the speaker's stand, bulky in his heavy gray overcoat, his scarf tucked around his throat, his white hair blowing in the winter wind.

He began to read his surprise poem, but something went wrong. The stiff wind tore at his papers and the glare of the sun made the letters dance before his eyes. He couldn't even see the words. He stumbled over them. His voice faltered, his hands trembled.

From the front row President and Mrs. John F. Kennedy, President Dwight D. Eisenhower, and all the other persons present watched in anxious sympathy. Lyndon B. Johnson, the new Vice-President, jumped up to help. He held out his top hat to cut off the sun and cast a shadow on the poet's papers. Perhaps this would help the famous poet.

But no. No one could help except Frost himself. Thousands in the audience held their breath in sympathy. Would the poet have to give up and sit down in failure?

Suddenly Frost gave up trying to read the new poem. He put the papers in his pocket, aware that he had promises to keep. Squaring his shoulders, he lifted his head with renewed courage. Then straight from the heart he said his old poem beginning, "The land was ours before we were the land's."

Now, full of spunk, Robert Frost stood sure and straight, braced against the wind and weather. His voice came clear and strong down through the very last line of "The Gift Outright,"

190

his poem about America: "Such as she was, such as she will become."

Millions of people, watching and listening in Washington and on television, felt a new surge of pride in their country. They felt pride, too, in this man of courage who spoke for them. Robert Frost was their poet, the poet of all America.

More About This Book

WHEN ROBERT FROST LIVED

1874   ROBERT FROST WAS BORN IN SAN FRANCISCO, CALIFORNIA, MARCH 26.

There were twenty-seven states in the Union.

Ulysses S. Grant was President.

The population of the country was approximately 43,750,000.

1874–   ROB LIVED WITH HIS FATHER, MOTHER, AND SIS-
1885   TER IN SAN FRANCISCO.

Alexander G. Bell invented the telephone, 1876.

Thomas Edison invented the phonograph, 1878, and the electric light bulb, 1879.

James A. Garfield became President and was assassinated, 1881.

Clara Barton founded the American Red Cross, 1881.

The civil service system in this country was begun, 1883.

The first electric railroad in America was operated in Baltimore, 1885.

1885– 1897	ROB LIVED IN NEW ENGLAND, ATTENDED SCHOOL, AND MARRIED ELINOR WHITE.

The American Federation of Labor was founded, 1886.

Thomas Edison invented the motion-picture camera, 1889.

Henry Ford built his first gas engine, 1893, and his first automobile, 1896.

1897– 1915	YOUNG FROST BECAME A FARMER, TAUGHT SCHOOL, AND LIVED BRIEFLY IN ENGLAND.

The Spanish-American War was fought, 1898.

Wilbur and Orville Wright flew the first heavier-than-air aircraft, 1903.

The Panama Canal was completed and opened to world traffic, 1914.

1915– 1963	FROST LIVED IN NEW ENGLAND, WROTE MANY POEMS, AND LECTURED IN COLLEGES.

World War I ended, 1918.

The League of Nations was founded, 1920.

The first full-length talking motion picture was made, 1927.

World War II was fought, 1939-1945.

Alaska and Hawaii became states, 1959.

194

1963 ROBERT FROST DIED IN BOSTON, MASSACHU-
SETTS, JANUARY 29.

There were fifty states in the Union.

John F. Kennedy was President.

The population of the country was approximately 189,450,000.

DO YOU REMEMBER?

1. How did Rob suddenly find out that he could whistle loud enough to be heard?

2. How did Rob get caught in a severe storm when the Frost family went to Cliff House?

3. What trick with eggs did Rob play on the others in Napa Valley?

4. How did Rob have fun with a magnifying glass when he visited the zoo?

5. How did Rob happen to meet Balso and his gang of boys?

6. Why did Rob become interested in politics when Grover Cleveland ran for President?

7. What trick with a card and a tack did Rob use to help his father campaign?

8. Why did the Frost family decide to spend the summer at Sausalito?

9. What kind of notebook did Rob keep after he moved to New England?

10. How did Charlie, Rob, and Sabra have fun swinging from tall slender birches?

11. Why did Rob dislike the Friday afternoon activities at school?

12. When did Rob write his first poem and where was it published?

13. How did Frost gradually acquire a great reputation as an American poet?

14. What happened when Frost recited a poem at the inauguration of President John F. Kennedy?

IT'S FUN TO LOOK UP THESE THINGS

1. What is a poet, and how does his writing differ from ordinary writing?

2. Why are poems sometimes more difficult to read than other kinds of writing?

3. Where are Dartmouth College and Harvard University, which Frost attended?

4. What other great poets once lived and wrote in New England?

5. What are the names of some of Frost's most popular poems?

6. Are most of Frost's poems best suited for adults to read or for children to read?

INTERESTING THINGS YOU CAN DO

1. Make a list of Frost's poems which you have read or which you would like to read.

2. Choose one of Frost's shorter poems to read aloud to the class.

3. Convert one of Frost's shorter poems to prose and read it to the class.

4. Make a drawing to illustrate one of Frost's poems to place on the bulletin board.

5. Compare Frost's poems with the poems written by another modern poet.

6. Write a few lines of poetry of your own, trying to imitate Frost's style of writing.

7. Start a scrapbook of poems, including a few poems written by Frost.

OTHER BOOKS YOU MAY ENJOY READING

Eugene Field: Young Poet, Kathryn Kilby Borland and Helen Ross Speicher. Trade and School Editions, Bobbs-Merrill.

John F. Kennedy: Young Statesman, Lucy Post Frisbee. Trade and School Editions, Bobbs-Merrill.

New England Country, Dorothy Wood. Childrens Press.

Story of San Francisco, Charlotte Jackson. Random House.

Time for Poetry, May Hill Arbuthnot, ed. Scott Foresman.

INTERESTING WORDS IN THIS BOOK

admiration (ăd′mĭ rā′shŭn) : feeling of esteem for another person or persons

agitated (ăj′ĭ tāt ed) : aroused, stirred up

bay window: small projection from a house containing a large window

bonny: lovely, appealing

cable car: special streetcar in San Francisco, pulled by a cable

198

canopy (kăn'ô pǐ) : spreading branches and leaves at the top

cobblestone (kŏb'l'stōn) : stone with rounded surface, formerly used for paving streets

contraption (kŏn trăp' shŭn) : machine, gadget

critter (krĭt'ēr) : creature, animal

croquet (krô kā') : game in which the players drive wooden balls with mallets

dray horses: horses formerly used to pull wagonloads of merchandise

enormous (ê nôr'mŭs) : immense, exceptionally large

Franklin stove: simple cast-iron stove invented by Benjamin Franklin

fraternity (fră tûr'nĭ tĭ) : organization or group of people banded together to help one another in some manner

freestone: flat stone which may be heated and used to warm a bed

hark: listen

inauguration day (ĭn ô'gǔ rā' shŭn dā') : day when a new president is sworn into office

indignantly (ĭn dĭg'nănt lĭ) : angrily, as if mistreated

omnibus (ŏm′nĭ bŭs) : public vehicle used to carry a number of people, a bus

Phi Beta Kappa (fī bā′ tà kăp′à) : fraternity made up of members who have secured exceptionally high grades

pucker (pŭk′ẽr) : pull together or tighten, as the lips in whistling

queue (kū) : braid of hair, worn at the back of the head

scudding (skŭd′ĭng) : moving swiftly as if driven by the wind

scythe (sīth′) : tool with a long handle and curved blade, used for mowing

sleek (slēk) : smooth and glossy

stag: male deer

tarried (tăr′ĭd) : waited

tortoise rim (tôr′tŭs rĭm′) : frame made from the shell of a tortoise or turtle

undertow: current beneath the surface along a beach that moves seaward when waves break at the shore

veranda (vĕ răn′dà) : roofed portico or porch attached to the outside of a building

wooden last: form shaped like the human foot, used to shape or repair shoes

200